MATHEMATICS ILLUSTRATED DICTIONARY

FACTS, FIGURES and PEOPLE
Including the NEW MATH

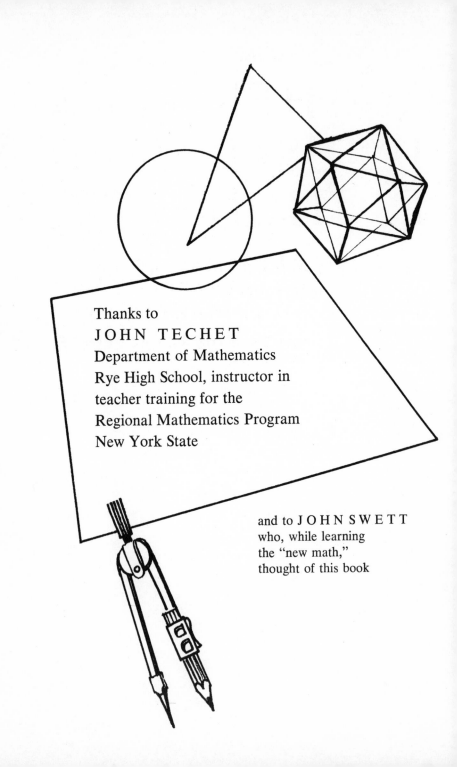

Thanks to
JOHN TECHET
Department of Mathematics
Rye High School, instructor in
teacher training for the
Regional Mathematics Program
New York State

and to JOHN SWETT
who, while learning
the "new math,"
thought of this book

MATHEMATICS ILLUSTRATED DICTIONARY

FACTS, FIGURES and PEOPLE
including the NEW MATH

by JEANNE BENDICK
and MARCIA LEVIN
in consultation with
LEONARD SIMON
Junior High School Curriculum Coordinator
Board of Education, New York City

illustrated by JEANNE BENDICK

McGRAW–HILL BOOK COMPANY
New York   Toronto   London   Sydney

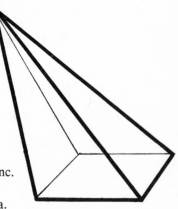

INTRODUCTION

Mathematics is one of the oldest and one of the youngest sciences. Not long ago to most people, its rules were rigid and its branches sharply separated. Now it has become recognized again as a living, growing subject, meaningful and exciting. In an exploration of the basic, logical structure of all mathematics, mathematicians and educators are expanding the world and the language of modern mathematics.

Mathematics is for young and old. It has been found that with a new approach to mathematical concepts, a six-year-old can learn basic ideas of algebra as easily as he can learn arithmetic. Traditional number skills have not been abandoned but they may be approached in a different way. Along with the old terms, new terms are used, sometimes to describe familiar ideas, sometimes to explain completely new concepts. These new terms are needed to convey complex ideas simply or to show the interrelationship of mathematical ideas.

The language of modern mathematics is precise and the meaning of words is carefully developed. Along with definitions, this book contains descriptions, explanations and many illustrations. There are also interesting mathematical problems and biographies of mathematicians, ancient and contemporary, whose work has contributed to our ever-broadening knowledge of the world we live in.

JEANNE BENDICK
MARCIA LEVIN
LEONARD SIMON

HOW TO USE THIS BOOK

Most terms appear in alphabetical order rather than under a general heading. For example, acute angle, obtuse angle, right angle appear under A, O and R, though they are mentioned and cross referenced under the general description of angle.

Cross references that are important to an understanding of any term are usually given in *italics*. If you are unfamiliar with descriptions of modern mathematics terms, it might be helpful to begin by looking up some of these words which appear over and over again, though not always as cross references.

arithmetic laws	notation system
axis	number
base of a numeration	number line
system	numeral
binary system	operation
coordinates	perpendicular
diameter	plane
endpoint	point
inequality	polygon
integer	sentence, mathematical
intersection	set
line segment	space figure

If you cannot find a word, it may be listed in a slightly different form. For example, you might be looking for approximate and find your description under approximation.

Some terms are commonly shortened. Positive may refer to positive integers; primes refer to prime numbers; solids mean solid or space figures.

Tables, symbols, abbreviations and formulas are at the back of the book, but they are also cross referenced with the text. For example, the description of a circle will also give you the page numbers where you will find formulas related to circles; the description of the metric system will refer you to the pages where you will find metric system tables.

The heading in the upper left-hand corner tells you what the first entry on each double page will be. The last entry on the facing page appears as the upper right-hand heading.

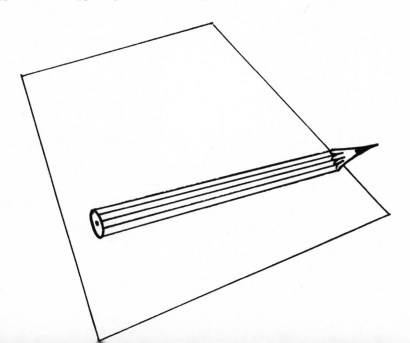

A

A. A is used to name a *point*.

It is used to name an *angle*.

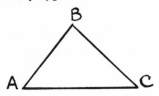

It is used to name the *vertex* of a *polygon*.

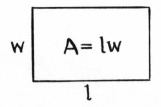

A is used to name a *set* of *elements*. A = {1, 2, 3}.
A is used in *formulas*.
  A = lw.

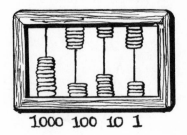

A can be the abbreviation for acre, area, altitude or other things.

a. a is used as a *variable* in a *formula*.

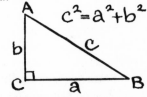

(PYTHAGOREAN THEOREM)

It is used to represent the measure of the side of a *polygon*.
It is used to name a *line*.

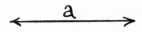

It is used in *equations,* as a *variable.* 2a = 18.
It is used to express general *properties.* For example, since the order of adding two numbers does not change the sum, the property may be stated: a + b = b + a.

abacus (ab′a-cus). An ancient calculating machine still used in Eastern countries to aid in

1000 100 10 1

arithmetic computation. It is made of beads strung on wires fastened into a frame. In elementary school it is used for teaching *place value*. Each wire has a place value and each bead has a *number value*.

Abel, Niels (ay′bel), 1802–1829. A Norwegian mathematician who studied group theory. He showed that the *roots* of a fifth-degree *equation* cannot be expressed by means of *radicals* in terms of the *coefficients* of the equation. He also did work with the binomial expansion and convergence, all before he died at 27.

Abelian group. See *commutative group*.

abscissa (ab-siss′a). The first number of an *ordered pair* of numbers called the *coordinates*, that locate a *point* on a *plane*. In the picture, 4 is the abscissa of point A in the plane. 4 is

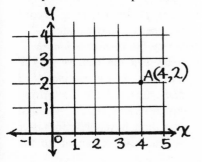

the distance from the *y-axis*. Point A's position or its address, is (4, 2). See *ordinate*.

absolute constant. See *constant*.

absolute difference. The difference between two numbers when the smaller number is subtracted from the larger. The absolute difference between 8 and 5 is 3.

absolute error. In measuring, the difference between *true length* and *measured length* is called the *error of measurement* or absolute error.

absolute unit. A unit that has an unchanging value at all times and places. We have set the *centimeter* as the absolute unit of length, the *gram* as the absolute unit of mass and the *second* as the absolute unit of time. Other units are based on this *cgs system*.

absolute value. The absolute value of a number, whether it is positive or negative, is always positive. The absolute value of zero is zero. Absolute value can be shown on the *number line* as the distance from the

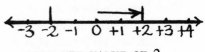

ABSOLUTE VALUE OF 2

point associated with the number to the zero point. The symbol for the absolute value of a number is a vertical bar on each side of the number:

$$|+5| = +5$$
$$|-5| = +5$$
$$|\ 0\ | = 0$$

absolute zero. In science, it is the total absence of heat, the temperature at which all thermal motion in matter stops. Theoretically it would be 273° below zero *centigrade* or 459° below zero *Fahrenheit*.

abstract. To remove an item or idea for emphasis, abridge; in *set theory* to single out a particular property which two or more sets, or the elements in one set, have in common.

abstract algebra. A study of algebra consisting of a *set* of *elements, operations* on these elements and a set of *axioms* or *postulates*. From these, other propositions are derived.

abstraction. The process of identifying common *properties*. Thus, whole number as a concept is based upon abstracting the common properties of *sets* of *elements*. For example, the legs of a bridge table and a

string quartet have the common element of "four-ness." From sets like these, we abstract the idea of the number four.

abstract number. Simply a number itself, without reference to any particular object or *set* of *elements*. *Numerals* are the written representations of abstract numbers.

abundant number or excessive number. A *positive integer* whose *factors* (except itself) add up to more than the integer. See also *aliquot part*.

24 IS AN ABUNDANT NUMBER

FACTORS

acceleration. The rate of change in *velocity* with respect to time.

account. A bookkeeping record of expenses and payments.

accuracy. See *measured length*.

Achilles and the tortoise (a-kill′ eez). One of the *paradoxes of Zeno*. It stated that if a tortoise has a head start on Achilles, even though Achilles runs faster he can never catch up to the tortoise in a race. While Achilles is making up the head start the tortoise goes a little distance, while Achilles makes up the little distance the tortoise goes another little distance, and so on. The paradox was not solved mathematically until the 19th century.

acre. A measurement of land in the United States and Great Britain, equal to 43,560 square feet, 4840 square yards or $\frac{1}{640}$ square mile.

actual value. The number for which a *numeral* stands.

actuary. A person who uses the branches of mathematics known as *probability* and *statistics* to set insurance rates.

acute angle. An angle whose measure is greater than 0° but less than 90°.

ACUTE ANGLES

ACUTE TRIANGLE

acute triangle. A triangle in which all three angles are acute.

addend. One of a set of numbers to be added. In $4 + 6 = 10$, 4 and 6 are addends and 10 is the *sum*.

adding machine. See *calculating machine.*

addition. A *binary operation* which pairs a number, the *sum*, with two other numbers, the *addends*. The symbol showing that the elements are to be added is $+$ (plus). To find the sum of two whole numbers such as 2 and 3, we may select two *disjoint sets* with separate or *discrete* elements:

$$A = \{a, b\} \quad B = \{c, d, e\}$$

One set has 2 elements, the other 3. If set $A = \{a, b\}$ and set $B = \{c, d, e\}$, their *union* consists of $\{a, b, c, d, e\}$.

$$A \cup B = \{a, b, c, d, e\}$$

A CUP B MEANS
"THE UNION OF SET A AND SET B CONTAINS a, b, c, d, e."

There are 2 elements in set A and 3 in set B and the number of elements in the union of sets A and B is 5. The sum of 2 and 3 is 5.

addition on the number line. Adding numbers on the *number line*.

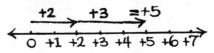

addition property of equality. For all *real numbers* a, b, c, if a = b, then a + c = b + c. See *equality*.

addition property of inequalities. For all *real numbers* a, b, c, if a < b then a + c < b + c. See *inequality*.

additive identity. In addition, the additive identity is zero. The sum of zero and any other number is the number itself.

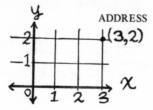

$$12 + 0 = 12$$
$$-3 + 0 = -3$$
$$a + 0 = a$$

See *commutative property*.

additive inverse.

$$12 + (-12) = 0$$
$$3 + (-3) = 0$$
$$a + (-a) = 0$$

For every *integer* there is another integer that, when added to it, gives a sum of zero. Either integer is called the additive inverse of the other. Zero has itself as its additive inverse. $0 + 0 = 0$.

address. The position of any *point* on a *plane*. See *abscissa*.

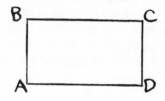

In a computer, the position of the tiny magnetic cores that store facts.

Adelard of Bath (ad'uh-lard), 12th century. An Englishman, widely traveled in the East, who first translated, in about A.D. 1120, *Euclid's Elements* of geometry from the Arabic into Latin.

adjacent. Lying next to. Adjacent angles are two angles in the same *plane* that have a common *vertex* and a common side. They have no interior points in common.

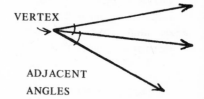

adjacent angles. See above.

adjacent sides. Sides of a *polygon* that have a common endpoint, or *vertex*.

In rectangle ABCD, side AB is adjacent to side BC.

adjoining. Touching, or having a common point, as adjoining triangles.

affine geometry. A kind of geometry in which a figure is projected by *parallel* rays to a plane which can be tilted.

ADJOINING
TRIANGLES

IN AFFINE GEOMETRY, THE RATIO BETWEEN
THE COLLINEAR POINTS DOES NOT CHANGE

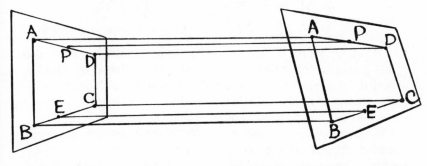

aggregate. The sum or total of a *collection*.

Ahmes (ah'mez) **or Ahmose,** about 1500 B.C. An Egyptian scribe, author of one of the oldest known mathematical texts, written about 3500 years ago. It contained ways for dealing with fractions and algebraic equations and explained how the circumference of a circle can be divided a fixed number of times by its diameter.

Aiken, Howard, 1900– A Harvard University professor who built the first working digital computer in 1944.

aleph null (ah'leff null). The set of natural numbers, 1, 2, 3 . . . goes on without end, so we say it is *infinite*. Any set of numbers that can be matched *one-to-one* with the natural numbers is said to have the *cardinal number* aleph null, which is written $\aleph_0$. The set of *common fractions* has the cardinal number aleph null. So does the set of all the even numbers, and the set of all the odd numbers. *Georg Cantor,* who invented the arithmetic of infinities, made up the term aleph null using the Hebrew letter for "a" and the Latin word for "none."

Alexandrian School. Another name for the Museum at Alexandria, founded about 300 B.C., which was the ancient world's center of learning for a thousand years. It was the first scientific institution supported by a government, and the most learned scientists studied and taught there. Euclid founded the school of mathematics at Alexandria.

algebra. The study of mathematical structure. Eleméntary algebra is the study of number systems and their *properties.* Algebra solves problems in arithmetic by using letters or symbols to stand for quantities. Algebra includes *calculus, logic,* the *theories of numbers, equations, functions* and combinations of these.

algebraic expression. An expression used in algebra such as the following:

a. A *numeral:* 3, .01, ¼, 10^3

b. A *variable:* a, x, y

c. The sum of any two *expressions:* a + b, x + 8

d. The difference of any two expressions: x − y, 14 − z

e. The *product* of any two expressions: 8y, ab, x^2, 7(m + n)

f. The *quotient* of any two expressions:

$$\frac{y^2}{x}, \frac{(a+5)}{-2}$$

See *polynomial, monomial.*

algebraic number. A number that can be produced by addition, subtraction, multiplication, division or *extracting* a *root* a *finite* number of times.

algorithm or algorism. A systematic procedure for carrying out a computation; any method of computing; step-by-step procedure.

aliquot part. Each of the *factors* of a number except the number itself. 3 is an aliquot part of 9.

Al Khowarizmi (al-co-war-reez′ me). A famous Arab algebraist who lived in the 9th century A.D. The word *algorithm* is taken from his name.

alpha. The first letter of the Greek alphabet; α is its symbol. The Greeks gave it a numerical value of 1.

alternate exterior angles. In geometry, the relationship of certain angles formed when parallel lines are *intersected* by a *transversal.*

Angles 2 and 7, 1 and 8 are alternate exterior angles.

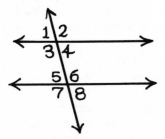

alternate interior angles. In the picture above, angles 3 and 6, 4 and 5 are alternate interior angles.

altimeter (al-tim′e-ter). An instrument for showing altitude or distance above sea level or land.

altitude. A *line segment* whose one *endpoint* is the *vertex* of a *polygon* and whose other endpoint *intersects* the side opposite the vertex, called the

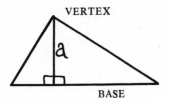

VERTEX

BASE

base. The altitude is *perpendicular* to the base. The letters a or h are used to denote the altitude or height of a polygon. Every triangle has 3 altitudes.

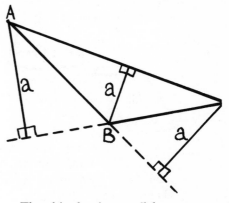

The altitude of a *parallelogram* is a line segment from any point on the opposite side perpendicular to a line containing the base (any side may be called a base).

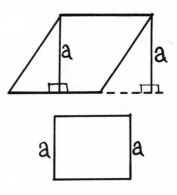

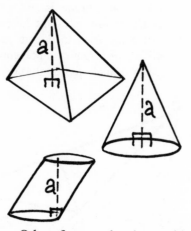

Other figures also have altitudes. The term altitude is sometimes used to mean the line segment and also its length.

Altitude is also the distance above the surface of the earth. See *table of formulas pp. 212–214.*

ambiguous. Not uniquely determined; having more than one meaning.

amicable numbers. Two numbers, each of which is equal to the sum of all the *factors* of the other number except the number itself. 220 and 284 are amicable numbers.

amount. The total of two or more sums. Also the sum of *principal* and *interest* at a certain date.

ampere. A measure of the rate of flow of electrical charges, named for André Ampere, a French mathematician and physicist.

analogue computer (an′a-log). A calculating machine that represents numbers by having them correspond to something else, such as length or voltage. The *slide rule* is an analogue computer.

analogy. A form of reasoning in which it is concluded that if things are alike in some respects, they are probably alike in other respects. This is not always true.

analysis. A part of mathematics using the methods of *algebra* and *calculus.* It deals with the infinitely large and the infinitely small.

In mathematical thought it is a process of starting at the conclusion and working backward. See *synthesis.*

analysis situs (a-nal′i-sis sy′tus). The technical name for *topology.*

analytic engine. A device invented about 1853 by Charles Babbage, an English mathematician, to solve mathematical problems. It was never completed because the engineering methods of the time were not far enough advanced, but it showed the way toward modern computers.

analytic geometry. Also called *Cartesian geometry*. The combining of geometry and algebra to name *points* on a *plane* with reference to a horizontal and a vertical axis. Points are named by *ordered pairs* called *coordinates;* graphs

VERTICAL AXIS

HORIZONTAL AXIS

COORDINATES

are drawn and curves are studied by means of *equations* and algebraic methods. Analytic geometry was developed by *René Descartes.* See also *abscissa, ordinate, x-axis, y-axis.*

Anaxagoras (an'ak-sag'o-ras), 500?–428 B.C. A philosopher-mathematician from Smyrna who did most of his work in Greece. While in prison (for saying that the sun was larger than Greece) he worked on *squaring the circle.* He is chiefly known as an astronomer.

and. A mathematical *connective.* A *compound sentence,* made up of two *simple sentences,* may be formed by using the word "and." If both simple sentences are true, the compound sentence is true. The symbol for "and" is $\wedge$. For example, $y < 5 \wedge 3 < y$ means that y is less than 5 and 3 is less than y. If y is 4, both simple sentences are true, since 4 is less than 5 and 3 is less than 4. 4 *satisfies* the connective $y < 5 \wedge 3 < y$.

The connective "and" when used as an *operation* on *sets* means the *intersection* of two or more sets.

$$\{a,b,c\} \wedge \{c,d,e,f\} = \{c\}$$

MEANS

THE INTERSECTION OF THESE SETS

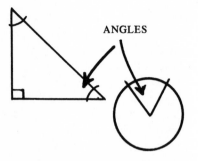

ANGLES

angle. A geometric figure made by two lines that intersect. The symbol for angle is ∠.

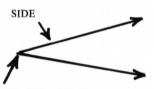

SIDE

THE VERTEX IS
A COMMON ENDPOINT

An angle is also described as the *union* of two *rays* having a common *endpoint*. The two rays are called the sides of the angle and the common endpoint is the *vertex*. See also *acute angle; adjacent angles; bisector* of an angle; *central angle, corresponding angle, elevation, angle of; exterior angle, interior angle; obtuse angle; right angle; straight angle.*

angstrom. A unit of length used to express wavelengths of light.

An angstrom is equal to 0.00000001 centimeter. 10,-000,000 angstroms equal 0.001 meter, or 0.04 inch. A° stands for angstrom.

annual. Once a year.

annular. Ring-shaped.

annulus (an'yuh-lus). The portion of the plane between two concentric circles, one of which is in the interior of the other.

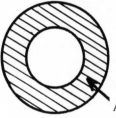

ANNULUS

antecedent. The first *term* of a *ratio*. In ratio 3:4, 3 is the antecedent.

In geometry, the first sentence of a *hypothesis*.

In logic, the sentence that is expressed by the "if" clause. If $2 + 2 = 4$, then $2 + 3 = 5$. In this sentence, $2 + 2 = 4$ is the antecedent.

antilogarithm. The antilogarithm of a given number is the number that has the given number as its *logarithm*. If log 3.42 = .5430, then antilog .5430 = 3.42. See *table pp. 222–223.*

antipodal points (an-tip'o-dal). The endpoints of a diameter of a sphere.

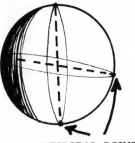

ANTIPODAL POINTS

apex. The highest point relative to some line or plane.

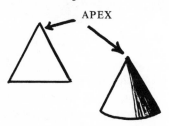

APEX

apogee (ap'o-gee'). The most distant or highest point, usually of an orbit.

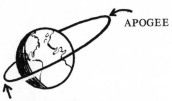

APOGEE

THE PERIGEE IS THE CLOSEST POINT

Apollonius (ap'o-lo'ni-us), 260–200 B.C. A Greek geometer whose work so completely detailed what was known that little was added to it for 1500 years. He is chiefly known for his work with *conic sections*. He was also a fine arithmetician and astronomer.

apothecaries' fluid measure (a-pahth'uh-care-ees). The liquid measure used in making drugs or prescriptions. See *table p. 218.*

apothecaries' weight. The standard weights and measures used for drugs. (Pharmacists also use the metric system.) See *table p. 216.*

REGULAR POLYGON

APOTHEM

INSCRIBED CIRCLE

apothem (ap'o-them). A *radius* (or length of radius) of the *inscribed circle* of a *regular polygon,* drawn perpendicular to a side of the polygon.

applied mathematics. Mathematics put to practical use, as in physics, mechanics or surveying, among others. When concepts of space and number are joined with time and matter, even relativity, magnetism and so on are considered applied mathematics.

approximation. A number that is not exact, but has been rounded off to a prescribed decimal place. Since no measurement is exact, all units of measure are approximations. An approximation of π is 3.14. See *error of measurement.*

Arabic numerals. The Hindu-Arabic numeration system used most commonly today:

0, 1, 2, 3, 4, 5, 6, 7, 8, 9

Arabs, mathematics of. From about the 9th to the 15th century A.D., the Arabs translated and kept alive the earlier Greek and Hindu writings that were later retranslated into Latin and English. Arab contributions were mainly in arithmetic and algebra.

arbitrary constant. See *constant.*

arc. A part of a circle. A *subset* of the set of *points* of a circle. In the drawing, points A and B are *endpoints* of minor arc AxB and major arc AyB. An arc that has the endpoints of a diameter as endpoints is called a semicircle. The symbol for arc is ⌒ .

arc and angle measurement. See *table p. 218.*

ARCHIMEDES

Archimedes of Samos (ar-ki-mee′deez), 287–212 B.C. One of the great mathematicians of all time. He gave *proofs* for finding the *areas, volumes* and centers of gravity for *circles, spheres, conics, spirals, curves* and *surfaces.* He began the sciences of *calculus,* of hydrostatics and of mechanics. A great inventor too, he discovered the laws of the lever and pulleys. He was one of the first to apply scientific thinking to everyday problems.

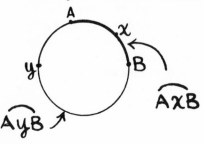

NETWORK

ARCS

arcs. In *topology,* the lines on a network. In Euler's *Königsberg Bridge problem,* each arc represented a bridge.

Arctic Circle. An imaginary circle on the earth, parallel to the equator. It is approximately 23°27′ from the North Pole.

are. A metric unit of area, 100 square meters; 119.6 square yards.

area. The amount of surface. The measure of a *closed region* of a *plane* is called its area. A standard unit of area is the square inch. There are formulas for finding the areas of many kinds of figures. See *table of formulas pp. 212–214.* See *volume* for three-dimensional figures.

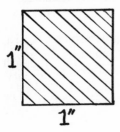

1 SQUARE INCH

area measure, surveyor's. The system of measurement used by surveyors. See *table p. 217.*

Aristarchus of Samos (ar′is-tar′kus), 280–264 B.C. Greek mathematician who was the first to work out the length of the year. He tried to calculate the distance from the earth to the moon and the sun, and concluded that the distance from the earth to the sun is some twenty times the distance from that of the earth to the moon.

Aristotle (ar′is-tot′l), 384–322 B.C. A great Greek philosopher who laid the foundations for most of the branches of science and philosophy known today. He had great influence on Western thinking, especially as a philosopher, political thinker and biologist.

arithmetic (a-rith′muh-tick). The branch of mathematics concerned with the study of the *positive real numbers* and *zero.* See *arithmetic laws.*

arithmetic, clock. See *modular arithmetic.*

arithmetic, fundamental theorem. Any *positive integer* can be *factored* into *primes* in only one way, apart from the order in which the prime factors are written. This *proposition* is called the fundamental theorem of arithmetic.

arithmetica (ah-rith-meh'ti-ca). The study of numbers, especially in ancient times, to find various interesting relationships between them.

arithmetic laws. There are 11 properties or laws for arithmetic:

The *closure property* for *addition*.

The *closure property* for *multiplication*.

The *commutative property for addition*.

The *commutative property for multiplication*.

The *identity property* for *addition*.

The *identity property* for *multiplication*.

The *associative property for addition*.

The *associative property for multiplication*.

The *inverse* property for *addition*.

The *inverse* property for *multiplication*.

The *distributive property*.

arithmetic mean (ar-ith-meh'tic) (called *average*). The mean or average of a set of numbers is found by dividing the sum of the numbers by the number of

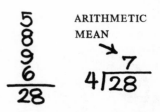

ARITHMETIC MEAN

numbers. See *central tendency*. Arithmetic mean or means may also refer to the other *terms* of an *arithmetic progression* of which the first and last terms are specified. The arithmetic mean of 8 and 10 is 9.

arithmetic number. A *subset* of the *real number* system; any real, *non-negative number*.

arithmetic operation. In common use, the four fundamental operations are *addition, subtraction, multiplication* and *division*. An operation applied to two *members* of a *set* identifies a third *element* of the set. For example, the operation addition, for 3 and 7, gives 10.

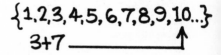

arithmetic progression. A *sequence* of numbers in which the same number is added each time. 1, 2, 3, 4 (1 is added). 1, 5, 9, 13 (4 is added). The number added is called the constant, or the *common difference*.

arrangement. A special way of setting out or ordering a collection of things, or the *members* of a *set*. A set of nine things, for example, might be

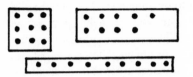

arranged in many ways. See *permutation*.

array. An orderly arrangement of objects in rows and columns. An egg carton is an example of a 2-by-6 array.

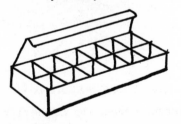

arrow in motion. One of the *paradoxes* of *Zeno,* which stated that, since the arrow is always in a given position at a given time, it is always at rest and never moves. (It is like separate frames in a strip of movie film, nothing moves in any

frame.) How, then, does an object move? The paradox was not answered for almost 2000 years.

arrows on lines and rays in geometry. Show that the *line* or *ray* extends infinitely in the direction of the arrow.

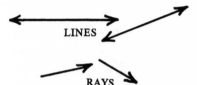

arrows to show one-to-one correspondence. See *mapping, one-to-one correspondence.*

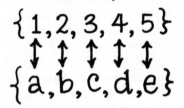

arrows used as symbols. *Connectives* in logic.

$$P \rightarrow Q$$

ascending. Increasing. In $x^2 + x^3 + x^4$, the exponents are in ascending order.

assessed value. The value assigned to property for the purpose of taxing it. Assessed value is usually only a certain percentage of the real value.

assets. The financial goods and property, resources of a business.

assigning. Matching or *associating* a number or letter with a point. The points on this line can be assigned numbers, like 1, 2, 3, 4 or letters like A, B, C, D.

$$\underset{\underset{A \quad B \quad C \quad D}{}}{\xleftrightarrow{\overset{1 \quad 2 \quad 3 \quad 4}{}}}$$

associating. Matching or *assigning*.

associative property for addition. The property by which *addends* may be grouped and added in any order, without changing the sum. $(1 + 2) + 3 = 6$. So does $1 + (2 + 3)$. In general, the property for all real numbers may be stated $(a + b) + c = a + (b + c)$.

associative property for multiplication. If any three numbers are multiplied in a given order, the *factors* may be grouped in any way without changing the product. $(2 \times 3) \times 4$ is the same as $2 \times (3 \times 4)$. The product of both is 24. In general, the property for all real numbers is
$$(ab)c = a(bc).$$

assumptions. A mathematical system depends upon a set of *propositions* which are assumed to be true. From these assumed propositions, other propositions may be deduced. Assumptions, in turn, are used to prove certain *theorems*. See *axiom, postulate*.

atomic number. The number of protons in each atom of an element. The atomic number determines the place of an element in the scale of elements.

8 PROTONS GIVE AN OXYGEN ATOM THE ATOMIC NUMBER 8

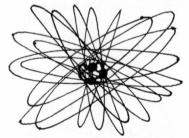

ITS ATOMIC WEIGHT IS 16

atomic weight. The weight of an atom, compared with the weight of an atom of oxygen, which is set at 16 atomic mass units. The atomic weight is usually about the same as the total number of protons and neutrons in its nucleus, which is called the mass number.

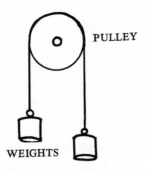

PULLEY

WEIGHTS

ATWOOD'S MACHINE

Atwood, George, 1746–1807. An English mathematician who wrote many books on mathematics. He invented Atwood's machine, which was used in the study of falling bodies, showing the relation of time, speed and motion under the force of gravitation.

automation. The use of modern computers or other electrical devices or machines to perform work and solve problems.

average. A single number representing a set of numbers. See *arithmetic mean*. It is one measure of *central tendency*. To find an average, see *table of formulas p. 215.*

average deviation. A measure used in *statistics* that shows how the *data* is grouped or spread about the measure of *central tendency*.

avoirdupois weight (av′er-du-poiz′). A system of weights used in the United States and Great Britain for all commodities except drugs, jewels and precious metals. See *table p. 216.*

axes, coordinate. The *x-axis* and the *y-axis,* used to locate *Cartesian coordinates.* See *abscissa, origin, axis, analytic geometry.*

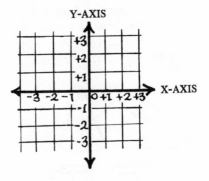

axial. Pertaining to an axis, or line.

axiom. Imagine mathematics as a set of statements. We accept certain statements to be true. From these first statements, other statements are then proved. The assumed statements are called axioms, *assumptions* or *postulates.* The geometry of *Euclid* was based on certain axioms which, centuries later, were recognized to be assumptions, and not "self-evident truths." Whole new geometries were invented by accepting different sets of axioms.

axis. The *number line* of a *graph* is called the *coordinate axis*. The horizontal number line is called the *x-axis*. The vertical number line is called the *y-axis*. Their point of intersection is called the *origin*.

Some geometric figures have axes. The axis of a *cone* is a *line segment* from the center of the *base* to the *vertex*.

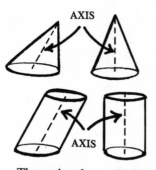

AXIS

AXIS

The axis of a *cylinder* is the *line segment* joining the center of the two *bases*.

An *ellipse* has two axes.

AXES

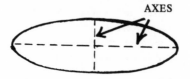

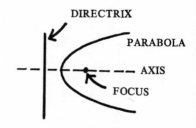

DIRECTRIX

PARABOLA

AXIS

FOCUS

axis of a parabola. A line about which both parts of a parabola are symmetrical.

axis of symmetry. The line about which a geometrical figure is symmetrical, such as the altitude of an equilateral triangle or the diameter of a circle. Imagine a drawing, folded along the axis. Every point on one half of the figure would fall on a point on the other side.

Two points are symmetric with respect to a line if the line is the *perpendicular bisector* of the line segment of which the points are the endpoints.

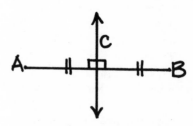

A AND B ARE SYMMETRIC TO LINE C

B

B. B is used to name a *point*.

It is used to name an *angle*.

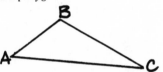

It is used to name the *vertex* of a *polygon*.

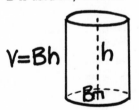

B is used to name a *set* of *elements*. B = {6, 7, 8, 9}.
B is used in *formulas*.

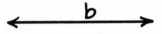

B is used as the abbreviation for *base*.

b. b is used as a *variable* in a *formula*.
It is used to represent the measure of a side of a *polygon*.

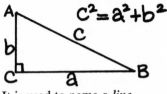

It is used to name a *line*.

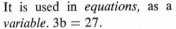

It is used in *equations,* as a *variable*. 3b = 27.
It is used to express general *properties*. For example, since the order of multiplying two numbers does not change the product, the property may be stated, a $\times$ b = b $\times$ a.

Babbage, Charles (bab′baj), 1792–1871. An English mathematician, engineer and inventor. He invented and solved codes of all kinds, devised a system of identifying lighthouses by the pattern of their beam and invented the first speedometer. He designed a *difference engine* for calculating logarithms to 20 decimal places and an *analytic engine* that was, in theory, much like today's computers. Babbage's ideas were so far beyond the engineering techniques of his time that neither machine could be successfully completed.

Babylonian numeration system. A *numeration system* used in ancient times, with a *base* of 60. The Babylonians wrote on clay, so their numerals were wedge-shaped. Their system looked like this:

Y	YY	YYY	YYYY	YYY YY
1	2	3	4	5

YYY YYY	YYYY YYY	YYYY YYYY	YYYYY YYYY
6	7	8	9

<	<Y	Y
10	11	60

60 is still the basis for our time system: 60 seconds = 1 minute; 60 minutes = 1 hour. Measurements in astronomy are based on 60 too.

ROGER
BACON

Bacon, Roger, 1214–1294. An English scientist whose ideas were so advanced that he was accused of magic. He said that mathematics was the alphabet of philosophy. He showed how astronomy and the other physical sciences rest on mathematics, and how it is only when their principles are stated in mathematical form that they progress.

balance. An equal distribution. Also, the amount owed on an article after a down payment has been made.

An instrument for weighing.

balance, bank. The amount of money in an account.

balance sheet. In bookkeeping, a listing of assets on the left side of the sheet and liabilities on the right side of the sheet. The sums of the two columns should balance.

ball. A *spherical* object or body.

ballistics. The study of the motion of projectiles, such as bullets or missiles.

bank discount. The money taken by the bank as interest on a loan, and deducted from the face value of the loan.

bank statement. A record of a checking account, usually issued to a depositor quarterly or monthly.

bar. The *line segment* used in a fraction to separate the numerator from the denominator.

$$\frac{3}{4} \leftarrow \text{BAR}$$

bar graph. See *graph*.

base as a factor. The number, symbol, or *variable* used with an *exponent*. In 6^4, 6 is the base. 6^4 means $6 \times 6 \times 6 \times 6$. The base is the number used as a *factor*.

base in percent. To find 30% of $47, 47 is the base, which is multiplied by the rate, .30. A formula that is often used is p = br. b is the base number and r is the percent number. See *table p. 215*.

base of a geometric figure. In the triangle below, the side opposite the vertex angle A is called the base of the triangle. The angles B and C are called the base angles.

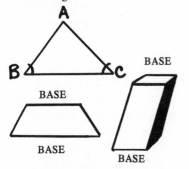

BASE

BASE

BASE

Many geometric figures have sides or portions of planes as their bases.

base of a numeration system. The number on which a numeration system is constructed. In our base ten system, 234 means 2 hundreds + 3 tens + 4 ones. The same symbols in a base five system mean 2 twenty-fives + 3 fives + 4 ones.

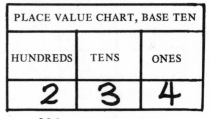

PLACE VALUE CHART, BASE TEN		
HUNDREDS	TENS	ONES
2	3	4

234, BASE $10 = 234$

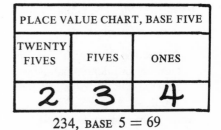

PLACE VALUE CHART, BASE FIVE		
TWENTY FIVES	FIVES	ONES
2	3	4

234, BASE $5 = 69$

base eight system. A numeration system, used by some computers, in which objects are grouped by eights. Also called the octal system.

base five system. In a base five system, objects are thought of as being grouped by fives. A base five or quinary system has five numerals, which might be 0, 1, 2, 3, 4. The word "five," written as a *subscript,* shows that grouping is in sets of five. For example, 22_{five} means 2 fives and 2 ones.

PLACE VALUE CHART, BASE FIVE		
TWENTY-FIVES	FIVES	ONES
	2	2

base ten system. See *decimal system.*

base two system. See *binary system.*

basic fraction. The simplest *fraction,* for example, $\frac{2}{3}$.

A fraction in which the numerator and denominator have no *common factor* other than 1 and −1.

basic pair. An *ordered pair* of *rational numbers* in which one member of the pair is zero.

basic table. Any operational table in arithmetic. It is made up of a grid of straight lines that form squares. The numerals in the squares show the results of the operations for which each table is designed.

bel. A unit of sound named for Alexander Graham Bell. Equal to 10 *decibels.*

bell-shaped curve. The normal curve of *distribution.* Notice that the greatest *frequency* occurs in the middle with a tapering off at each end.

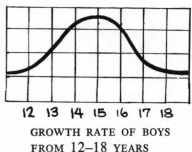

GROWTH RATE OF BOYS
FROM 12–18 YEARS

Beltrami, Eugenio, 1835–1900. Italian mathematician, famous for his work on *non-Euclidean geometry,* electricity and magnetism. He was the inventor of the *pseudosphere,* on which the geometry of *Lobachevski* is based.

BASIC ADDITION TABLE TO $3 + 3 = 6.$ WHERE THE LINES INTERSECT IS THE SUM OR ANSWER, $3 + 2 = 5$

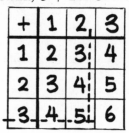

+	1	2	3
1	2	3	4
2	3	4	5
3	4	5	6

beneficiary. The person named by the owner of a life insurance policy as the one to whom the value of the policy should be paid when the insured dies.

Bernoulli (ber-noo'yee) **or Bernouilli.** A Swiss family which, from 1654 to 1782, produced eight great mathematicians. The most famous were the versatile brothers Jakob and Johann, both teachers. They were among the first to understand the importance of the *differential* and *integral calculus,* and they established fundamental principles in *probability.* Daniel, the son of Johann, won ten prizes from the French Academy of Sciences.

beta. The second letter of the Greek alphabet and the Greek name for their numeral 2. The symbol for beta is β.

between. Refers to an *interval* which does not include the first and last *elements.* For example, "The set of whole numbers between 3 and 7," would mean the numbers 4, 5 and 6.

betweenness. See *density.*

Bhaskara (bus'kah-rah), 1114–1185. A Hindu mathematician who wrote the "Lilāvati"

(named in honor of his daughter) and several other important books on mathematics. He developed the rules related to zero, which he called "cipher."
1. If cipher is added to a number, the sum is the same as the number.
2. If cipher is subtracted from a number, the result is still the number itself.
3. If a number is multiplied by cipher, the result is cipher. He also introduced the idea of *negative numbers* and of the *additive inverse.*

bi. A prefix meaning two or twice, as bilateral, biangular or binary.

biconditional. In a *compound sentence,* if the *connective* is in the form of "if and only if," the statement is called biconditional. The symbol for biconditional is written

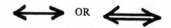

billion. A thousand millions in the United States, a million millions in Great Britain.

binary operation (by'na-ry). An operation performed on two *elements* at a time. Addition and multiplication are both binary operations. For example, you can add 23 + 64, and you can multiply 23 and 64.

binary system. A numeration system that uses only two numerals, usually 0 and 1, to express all numbers. Only the use of *place value* makes this possible. Many electronic computers operate under the binary system, sometimes called dyadic notation.

binomial. A binomial is the algebraic *sum* of two *monomials*. Some examples of binomials are: $2 + 3$, $x + 1$, $2x - 1$, $3x - 4y$, $m^2 - 2m$. See *polynomial*.

binomial distribution. A *distribution* of a number of successes in a series of trials where each trial can end in either success or failure. Counting the number of times a tossed coin turns up heads or tails is this kind of trial.

PLACE VALUE CHART BASE TWO (BINARY SYSTEM)				
EIGHTS $(2 \times 2 \times 2)$	FOURS (2×2)	TWOS (2)	ONES	NUMBER
			0	← 0
			1	← 1
		1	0	← 2
		1	1	← 3
	1	0	0	← 4
	1	0	1	← 5

IN THE BINARY SYSTEM, 5 IS 101, BASE TWO
8 IS 1000, BASE TWO
15 IS 1111, BASE TWO

binomial theorem. A rule for writing out an *equivalent* expression such as $(a + b)^2$ without having to perform all the multiplication involved. The answer, in this case $a^2 + 2ab + b^2$, was first shown by *Omar Khayyam,* then by *Descartes* and *Newton.* In the binomial theorem, the *coefficient* of the first and last terms is 1, and the coefficient of the second and next-to-last terms is the same as the *exponent.* The number of terms written out is one more than the exponent. For example, $(a + b)^5$ is
$$a^5 + 5a^4b + 10a^3b^2 + 10a^2b^3 + 5ab^4 + b^5$$

biometry (bi-om'eh-tree). The application of mathematics, especially *statistics,* to the study and measurement of living things.

bisect. To cut or divide into two equal parts.

bisector. In geometry, a straight *line segment* which divides another line segment, or an angle, into two equal parts.

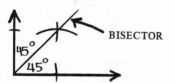

BISECTOR

bit. The shortened term for binary digit, either 1 or 0.

body of a matrix. The part of a table which shows the results of the operation. See *matrix.*

Boethius (bo-ee'thee-us), A.D. 475–525. A Roman philosopher who translated the works of the ancient mathematicians and bridged the gap between the knowledge of the Greeks and that of the middle ages.

Bolyai, Johann (bol'yai, yo' hahn), 1802–1860. Hungarian mathematician who at the age of 22 wrote "Absolute Science of Space," a complete system of geometry. He showed that *Euclid's parallel postulate* was not necessary and that a whole system of geometry could be based on the *pseudosphere* of *Beltrami.* Although he was one of the founders of *non-Euclidean geometry,* he had been preceded (unknown to him) by *Gauss* and *Lobachevski.*

Bolyai, Wolfgang (bol'yai, vohlf' gang), 1775–1856. Father of *Johann Bolyai.* He studied with *Gauss* and tried to prove *Euclid's parallel postulate.*

bookkeeping. The work of keeping the account books and records of a business firm.

GEORGE
BOOLE

Boole, George (bool′), 1815–1864. An Englishman who helped develop modern symbolic *logic*. He was one of the first mathematicians to realize that *symbols* of *operation* could be separated from those of *quantity*. He showed that classes or sets of objects could be operated on in the same way algebraic symbols or numerical quantities can. Boole applied ordinary algebra to the logic of *classes*. One of the many modern applications of Boolean algebra is its use in the design of electronic computers. Boole also applied his laws of reasoning to the mathematics of *probability,* and produced a view of an abstract *calculus.*

Boolean algebra (bool′ee-an). The beginning of the algebra of logic, formulated in 1847 by George Boole. It has two main divisions: the algebra of *classes* and the algebra of relations. He is also credited with formulating *axioms* in the algebra of *sets.*

borrowing. A term formerly used in connection with subtraction. In modern language, a number is *renamed* and then the subtraction process is carried out.

$$64 = 60 + 4 = 50 + 14$$
$$-39 = 30 + 9 = 30 + 9$$
$$20 + 5 = 25$$

64 is renamed $50 + 14$.

boundary. A boundary can be:
1. A *point* that separates a *line* into two *half-lines.*

BOUNDARY

2. A line that separates a *plane* into two *half-planes.*

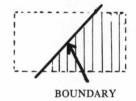

BOUNDARY

3. A plane that separates *space* into two *half-spaces.*

4. The set of points of a closed figure that separates a plane into two *regions*.

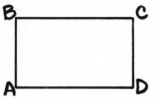

RECTANGLE ABCD IS THE
BOUNDARY OF ITS INTERIOR

A boundary separates a plane into three sets of points: the interior set, the exterior set and the set which makes up the boundary.

$$\{ \quad \} \quad \text{BRACES}$$

braces. Used in *set notation* to identify the *elements* of a set. The braces also stand for the word "set," when reading or writing about sets.

$$A = \{1, 2, 3\}$$

The set A contains members 1, 2 and 3.

brackets. Brackets, like parentheses, indicate that the quantities enclosed are to be treated as a unit. $2 \times [6 - (2 \times 2)] = 4$.

$$[\quad] \quad \text{BRACKETS}$$

TYCHO
BRAHE

Brahe, Tycho (brah'eh, tie'ko), 1546–1601. A Scandinavian mathematician and astronomer who made the largest and most accurate collection of astronomical facts prior to the invention of the telescope. He left his table of planetary motions for *Kepler* to finish. The Imperial mathematician to Emperor Rudolph II, Brahe is said to have lost the tip of his nose in a duel over a geometry problem. He discovered and measured the position of a brilliant star now called Tycho's star. His name is also given to one of the craters of the moon. In his theory of the universe, the earth was the center.

Briggs, Henry (or Harry), 1561–1630. An English professor of geometry who recognized the importance of the *logarithms* of *Napier,* and originated the work which led to the use of 10 as the base for the tables of logarithms. See *table pp. 222–223.*

broken line. A union of *line segments* joined end to end, but not in a straight line. Not more than two segments have a common *endpoint.*

broken‑line graph. A diagram showing how an *ordered pair* of items are related by connecting points on a grid with line segments.

TEST RECORD

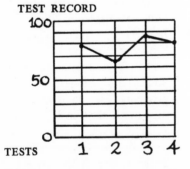

TESTS

Brouwer, Luityen (brow'er, light' ain), 1881–   . A Dutch mathematician who made great contributions to *topology* and the theory of *sets*. Brouwerian mathematics states that intui-

tion can help to solve mathematical problems.

Brouwer's problem. States that a map of three countries can be constructed so that every point along the boundary of each country is a meeting place of all three countries. Although this map is impossible to draw, it is possible to show mathematically that it can be constructed.

Buffon needle problem. An experiment in *probability* by the Comte de Buffon, an 18th-century French mathematician. He showed that if a needle is dropped on a flat surface which has parallel lines on it, the number of times the needle falls across a line closely approximates the value of *pi* (π). The parallel lines are set a distance apart. The length of the needle is such that $l < d$. The probability that the needle will intersect one of the lines is $p = 2\ 1/\pi d$.

THE NEEDLE MUST BE SHORTER THAN THE DISTANCE BETWEEN THE LINES

**VANNEVAR
BUSH**

Bush, Vannevar, 1890–   . American engineer, mathematician and physicist who, in 1931, built the first large modern *analogue computer.* He coordinated the scientific research on the atomic bomb project and was director of the U.S. Office of Scientific Research and Development during World War II.

bushel. A unit of *dry measure,* containing 4 *pecks.* See *table p. 218.*

C

C. C is used to name a *point.*

It is used to name an *angle.*

It is used to name the *vertex* of a *polygon.*

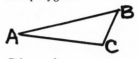

C is used to name a *set* of *elements.* C = {8, 9, 10}.
C is used in *formulas.*

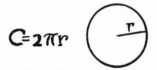

C is the Roman numeral for 100.

C is the abbreviation for *centigrade* and for *circumference.*

c. c is used as a *variable* in a *formula.*

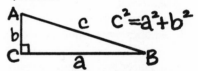

It is used to represent the measure of the side of a *polygon.*

It is used to name a *line.*

It is used in *equations,* as a *variable.* 3c = 9.

It is used to express general *properties.*

$$a(bc) = a(cb).$$

c is the abbreviation for the speed of light.

calculating machines. Devices that solve problems in arithmetic: addition, subtraction, multiplication and division. All calculating machines were developed from the adding machine, which is the simplest. *Computers* are complicated calculating machines. See also *Pascal.*

calculation. The act of computing or figuring.

calculate. To get a result by carrying out a mathematical process.

calculus. Calculus was discovered in the 17th century, independently by *Isaac Newton* of England and *Gottfried Leibniz* of Germany. It is a field of mathematics with tremendous applications to physics, chemistry, engineering, biology, economics and many other areas. Basic to calculus is the idea of *limit.* Calculus deals with changing quantities and with motion. In *differential calculus,* the idea of limit allows us to find the instantaneous rate of change (called the derivative) of a *function,* which is like a formula. *Integral calculus* is used to find the work done by a force, and to solve geometric problems. *Archi-*

medes was one of the first to use a kind of calculus.

calendar. A method of measuring and recording time, especially in cycles of a year, including the arrangement of days into weeks and of weeks into months. Most calendars are based on the solar year, the time it takes the earth to make one complete orbit around the sun. Some calendars are based on the lunar month, from one new moon to the next.

calibration. The marking off of an instrument into units for measuring.

calipers. Instruments for measuring dimensions, the thickness or diameter of an object or the distance between surfaces. Some calipers are a graduated rule with one sliding part and one fixed part. Some have two legs, usually curved.

VERNIER CALIPERS

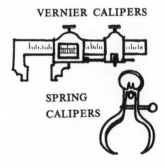

SPRING CALIPERS

cancel. To add equal quantities to both *members* of an *equation;* to divide out a *factor* common to both *terms* of a *fraction.*

candle power. The standard measure of light set by international agreement. The brightness of electric lights is measured in candle power.

GEORG
CANTOR

Cantor, Georg, 1845–1918. A German mathematician born in St. Petersburg, Russia. He taught at the University of Halle from 1869–1913. He is known for his work on the theory of numbers, particularly infinite classes. He introduced the term transfinite numbers and the symbols to represent them, starting with *aleph null.*

cap. The symbol for *intersection* of *sets.* A ∩ B is read, "A cap B," or "the intersection of A and B."

capacity. The number of *cubic units* a container can hold,

which is called the *volume* of the container.

Cardano, Girolamo (kar-da′no), 1501–1576 (called Cardan). An Italian mathematician who, by a ruse, forced *Tartaglia* to teach him his method of solving a *cubic equation,* which he published as his own. Although it was later proved to be Tartaglia's, the solution is still known as "Cardan's solution of the cubic." Cardano also recognized the importance of negative *roots.*

cardinality of a set. The number of *elements* in a *set,* without regard to the kinds of elements the set contains. If set

R = {a, b, 3, 5},

then the cardinal number of set R is 4.

cardinal number. A number that describes how many are in a *set* of things. Two sets have the same cardinal number if the *elements* in the sets can be matched one-to-one. Each of these sets has the cardinal number 2.

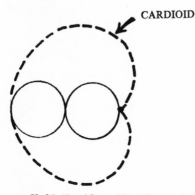

CARDIOID

cardioid (kar′dee-oid). If one circle is stationary and a second circle of equal size rolls around it, the path made by a point on the moving circle is called a cardioid.

caret (ca′ret). A mark, $\wedge$, often used in division, when the decimal points in the *divisor* and in the *dividend* are both "moved" the same number of places to the right.

To express numbers in *scientific notation,* for example, in 93000000, a caret is placed after the first *significant digit:* $9_\wedge 3000000$. This helps us find the *exponent.*

$9_\wedge 3000000 = 9.3 \times 10^7$.

Carroll, Lewis, 1832–1898. The pseudonym of Charles Lutwidge Dodgson, English writer and mathematician. He lectured in mathematics at Ox-

ford, wrote on Euclid and invented many mathematical brain-teasers. His mathematical writing is overshadowed by his famous "Alice in Wonderland."

LEWIS CARROLL

carrying. A *computational* process used in addition when the sum of a column is as great or greater than the *base* used. For example, in our base ten system, whenever the sum of a single column is more than 9, the last *digit* of the sum is written under that column and the remaining figures are added to the *addends* of the next column to the left. Carrying is now often called *regrouping.* For example, 14 ones are regrouped as 1 ten and 4 ones.

Cartesian coordinates. Every point in a *plane* is given an *address.* This address is a pair of numbers, the first of which is called the *abscissa.* The numbers associated with the point are called the *coordinates* of the point.

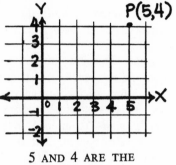

5 AND 4 ARE THE
COORDINATES OF · P

Cartesian geometry (kar-tee′see-yan). Usually called *analytic geometry. René Descartes* and *Pierre de Fermat* worked independently on it. Basically it is the joining of geometry and algebra. A correspondence is developed so that curves can be studied in terms of their *equations.*

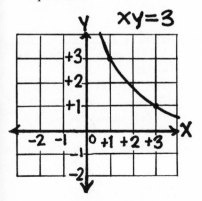

Cartesian set or product. The *set* of all *ordered pairs,* made by matching every element in a first set with every element in a second set. If the first set, A, consists of the numbers 1 and 2, and the second set, B, consists of the numbers 3, 4 and 5, then the Cartesian product or set, $A \times B$, consists of $(1, 3)$, $(1, 4)$, $(1, 5)$, $(2, 3)$, $(2, 4)$ and $(2, 5)$. See *cross.* The members of A are the first *components* of the ordered pairs, and the members of B are the second components of the ordered pairs. Notice that in set A there are 2 elements, in set B there are 3 elements and in their Cartesian product there are 6 elements.

catenary. The curve formed by a string or chain, hanging from two fixed points.

CATENARY

Cauchy, Augustin Louis (koh′ shee′), 1789–1857. French mathematician who was professor at three colleges in Paris at the same time. His work was influential in every branch of mathematics, especially in *calculus,* the theory of functions and algebraic *analysis.* He published almost 800 writings.

Cavalieri, Francesco (kav-al-yeh′ ri), 1598–1647. Italian mathematician and Jesuit priest who taught at Bologna. He invented the method of indivisibles, which was the forerunner of integral calculus. Cavalieri's theorem is concerned with solids of equal volume.

Cayley, Arthur, 1821–1895. English mathematician who taught at Cambridge. He worked in pure mathematics, especially the theory of *matrices* and the theory of *invariants.*

cc. Abbreviation for *cubic centimeter.*

Celsius scale (sell′see-us). The *centigrade* thermometer scale, first proposed by Swedish astronomer Anders Celsius.

cent. A penny, the 100th part of a U.S. dollar.

center. In a circle, the *point* in the *plane* which is equidistant from all points on the *circle.* A *line segment* from the center to the circle is called a *radius.* Radii of a circle are all equal in length.

center of a sphere. A *point* equally distant from all points on the *sphere.*

centesimal. Division into 100 equal parts, usually referring to a system of measuring angles. In the centesimal system a *right angle* is divided into 100 parts or degrees; a degree is divided into 100 angular minutes; a minute is divided into 100 angular seconds. In this system, which is not in common use, a circle has 400 centesimal degrees instead of the usual 360°.

centi. A prefix meaning 100.

centigrade scale. One method for measuring temperature in degrees. On the centigrade scale the freezing point of water is 0° and the boiling point is 100°.

centigram. $\frac{1}{100}$ of a *gram,* equal to 0.1543 *grain.* See *table pp. 219–220.*

centiliter. $\frac{1}{100}$ of a *liter,* equal to 0.6102 *cubic inch* or 0.338 U.S. *fluid ounce.* See *table pp. 219–220.*

centimeter. $\frac{1}{100}$ of a *meter,* equal

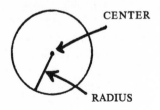

CENTER

RADIUS

to 0.3937 inch. See *table pp. 219–220.*

central angle. An angle with its *vertex* at the center of a circle.

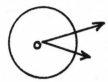

central tendency, measures of. In *statistics,* the terms mean (or average), median and mode are all ways of indicating the place on a *distribution curve* where the largest number of items are concentrated. If the average mark on an exam is 80, that is the mean. If half the class had a mark above 75, that is the median; if more students had 85 than any other score, that is the mode. These are all measures of central tendency.

century. One hundred years.

cgs system. The *metric system* of measurement in which the three fundamental units are the *centimeter,* the *gram* and the *second.* See *absolute unit.*

chain measure. A system of measurement used by surveyors. See *table p. 217.*

chance. See *probability.*

change of base. A numeral such as 13 in *base ten* may be changed to 23 in *base five.* Both numerals represent the same number.

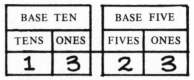

BASE TEN		BASE FIVE	
TENS	ONES	FIVES	ONES
1	3	2	3

characteristic. See *logarithms.*

checking. A method of showing whether or not a solution is correct. The method for checking subtraction is addition. See also *proof.*

$$\begin{array}{r} 97 \\ -63 \\ \hline 34 \end{array} \qquad \begin{array}{r} 34 \\ +63 \\ \hline 97 \end{array}$$

chevron. The symbol $>$ (is *greater than*) or $<$ (is *less than*). It can be written $\geq$ (is greater than or *equal* to), or $\leq$ (is less than or equal to).

Chinese, early mathematics of. The early Chinese were fine mathematicians. Almost 5000 years ago they had a numeration system based on two numbers, like the *binary system* used now in digital computers.

chord. A *line segment* whose endpoints are on the circle. See also *diameter.*

CHORD

chronology. The science of arranging time in periods and establishing the dates and historical order of past events.

chronometer. A very precise clock, accurate to within a second or two over a period of months. It is used mainly aboard ships to help determine their position at sea.

ciphers. See *codes, numerals, zero.*

circle. A *set* of all *points* in a *plane* at a fixed distance from a fixed point in the plane. The fixed point is called the center or focus of the circle.

A circle divides a plane into 3 sets of points:

1. The set of all points outside the circle,

2. The set of all points inside the circle,

3. The set of all points on the circle.

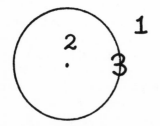

circle, area of. See *table p. 212.*

circle, great. The *intersection* of a *sphere* and a *plane* that passes

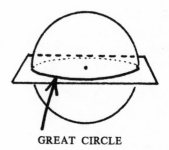

GREAT CIRCLE

through the center of that sphere.

circle, small. The *intersection* of a *sphere* and a *plane* that does not pass through the center of the sphere.

SMALL CIRCLE

circle, squaring the. Squaring the circle is one of the most famous problems in the history of mathematics. Using only a *straightedge* and *compass,* ancient geometers tried to construct a square equal in area to a given circle and found it impossible. To square the circle, a *line segment* of length $\sqrt{\pi}$ must be constructed from a unit line segment. In 1882 it was shown that π and $\sqrt{\pi}$ are not *algebraic*. Any length constructable by straightedge and compass from a unit segment is algebraic; therefore it is impossible to square the circle in terms of Euclidean geometry.

circle graph. See *graph.*

circular closed region. The *union* of a circle and its *interior.*

CIRCULAR CLOSED REGION

circular measure. See *table p. 218.*

circumference. The measure of the distance around a circle. See *table of formulas p. 212.*

circumscribe. A circumscribed circle is a circle passing through all the *vertices* of a *polygon.*

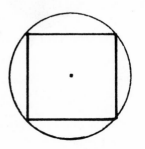

class. A collection of things. It may be the class of all the whole numbers, or the class of all boys named Steve, or the class of stars larger than the sun. The class may be *finite,* like the class of red-headed grocers in a town, or it may be *infinite,* like the class of fractions.

Mathematicians also call a class a set, a collection, an aggregate or a manifold.

clock arithmetic. See *modular arithmetic.*

clockwise. The direction in which clock hands travel.

closed broken line. A figure formed when the starting point of the broken line intersects its endpoint. The *line segments* may intersect each other on the line segment. See *closed plane figure.*

CLOSED BROKEN LINES

closed curve. A *curve* which starts at a point and comes back to that point.

closed interval. A set of numbers consisting of two given numbers and all the numbers between them.

closed plane figure. A figure that starts at a *point* and comes back to the point.

SIMPLE CLOSED FIGURES

NOT A SIMPLE CLOSED FIGURE

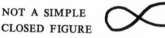

A simple closed figure separates the *plane* into the *set* of *points* on the figure, those outside the figure and those inside the figure.

closed region. The *union* of a *simple closed curve* and its *interior*.

CLOSED REGION

closed sentence. A *sentence* in mathematics which does not contain a *variable*.

closed set. If the answer to an operation is an *element* in the given *set*, the set is closed. Set A is closed under the operations of addition and multiplication. Any 2 elements in the set can be added or multiplied and the sum or product is a member of set A.

Set A is the infinite set of all the counting numbers.

$$A = \{1, 2, 3, 4, 5 \ldots\}$$

See *closure, property of.*

closed-space figure. A figure made up of a *set* of *points* in *space* which separates space into the set of points inside the figure, the set of points outside the figure and the set of points on the figure.

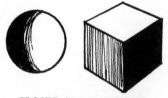

CLOSED-SPACE FIGURES

closure, property of. If a *binary operation* on any two *elements* in a given *set* produces a result that is also an element in the set, the set is said to be closed under that operation. The set of whole numbers is closed for addition and multiplication. If you take any two whole numbers, their product is another whole number. The set of whole numbers is not closed under subtraction or division. For example, 8 − 9 is not a whole number; neither is 5 ÷ 3.

cm. Abbreviation for *centimeter*.

coaxial (koh-ax′ee-uhl). Having a common *axis*.

codes (and ciphers). Methods of writing secret messages so that they can be read only by people who know the key. The two main systems for making up codes are substitution and transposition. In substitution the actual letters of the message are replaced by other letters, numbers or symbols:

H	E	L	P
8	5	12	16

In transposition the positions of the letters are changed according to some pattern. All codes can be "broken" mathematically. Computers are used for code-breaking because they can work their way through all the mathematical possibilities much more quickly than people can.

coefficient. In the *term* 5x, 5 is the coefficient of x. Generally, the coefficient is the *product* of all the *factors* of a term except one. For example, in $5x^2y$, the coefficient of y is $5x^2$.

coin-tossing. A simple way to demonstrate how *probability* works.

collateral. Property pledged for a *loan*.

collection. A *group* or *set*, such as a collection of dolls or a collection of whole numbers.

collinear points (koh-lin′ee-uhr). A *set* of *points* that are contained in the same line.

column. A vertical arrangement, such as a column of numbers to be added. In a *matrix,* columns are vertical and rows are horizontal.

2
3
6   COLUMN
7

combination. Statement of addition or multiplication facts. A whole number less than 10 and another whole number less than 10 equal a sum or a product, depending on the operation. $3 + 3 = 6$. $3 \times 3 = 9$.

combinations in statistics. A set of objects selected without reference to the order in which they are arranged. If you select 3 out of a set of 4 books (titled A, B, C and D) without regard to their order, there are 4 possible combinations: ABC, ABD, ACD, BCD. See also *permutations*.

combining. See *union, intersection, addition.*

commensurable. Having a common *divisor* or a common measure.

commission. A *percentage* given to an agent for his service in selling a product.

common denominator. A *common multiple,* usually the *least common multiple* of the *denominators* of a number of *fractions*. A common denominator of

is their common multiple, 12. It is also the *least common denominator* in this case.

common difference. The difference between any *term* and the preceding term of an *arith-*

metic *progression*. For example, in the arithmetic progression 7, 11, 15, 19, the common difference is 4.

common divisor. A quantity that is a *factor* of two or more numbers, quantities or expressions.

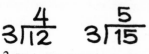

3 IS A COMMON DIVISOR OF 12 AND 15

common factor. A *common divisor.*

common fraction. (Also called rational number.) A *fraction* in which the *numerator* and *denominator* are both *integers*.

COMMON FRACTION

common logarithm. *Logarithms* having 10 as a *base*. See *Briggs, Henry.*

common multiple. A *multiple* of each of two or more quantities. See *least common multiple.*

common ratio. See *geometric progression.*

commutative group (kom-mu′ tah-tiv) (or Abelian group). A *set* of elements with the following *properties:*
1. The system has *closure.*

2. The *operation* is *associative*.

3. The operation is *commutative*.

4. It has an *identity element*.

5. For every element there is an *inverse element*.

commutative property of addition. A law of mathematics that says the order in which you add numbers does not affect the sum. In general, for all numbers a and b, $a + b = b + a$. $4 + 3$ always equals $3 + 4$.

commutative property of multiplication. A law of mathematics that says the order in which you multiply numbers does not affect the product. $4 \times 3 = 12$, $3 \times 4 = 12$. $4 \times 3 = 3 \times 4$. In general, for all numbers a and b, $ab = ba$.

comparing. We may compare 8 and 2 by subtraction. 8 is 6 more than 2. We may compare them by division. 8 is 4 times as much as 2. Comparing in arithmetic usually involves the operations of subtraction and division.

comparison property. For any two numbers, 8 and 6, either $8 = 6$, $8 > 6$ (8 is greater than 6) or $8 < 6$ (8 is less than 6). In general, for any real numbers a and b, exactly one of the following statements is true: $a = b$, $a > b$, $a < b$.

compass. In geometric construction, an instrument used to draw a circle and to mark off equal lengths.

complementary angles. Two angles whose sum is a right angle.

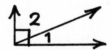

$\angle 1$, COMPLEMENT OF $\angle 2$
$\angle 2$, COMPLEMENT OF $\angle 1$

complementary set. When a given *set* contains a *subset,* all *members* of the set not in the subset belong to the complementary set.

If set A = {1, 2, 3, 4, 5}, and a subset B = {2, 3, 5}, then the complementary set to B is {1, 4}.

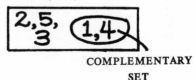

COMPLEMENTARY
SET

complementation. An operation on a *set* and a *subset*. The symbol for complementation may be written A′, ~A, Ā.

complete factorization of a number. The given number expressed as the *product* of *prime numbers*.

$$12 = 3 \times 2 \times 2$$

completeness. A *property* of a mathematical system in which any proposition can either be proved or disproved.

completeness property of the set of real numbers. For every point on a *number line* there is a *real number,* and for every real number there is a point on the number line.

completing the square. A process that makes it possible to *factor* some *polynomials*. It is helpful in solving *quadratic equations*.

complex fraction. A *fraction* whose *numerator* and/or *denominator* contains fractions.

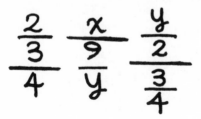

complex number. The sum of a *real number* and an *imaginary number,* such as 3 + 2i. Complex numbers have the form a + bi, where a and b are real numbers and i is imaginary. The idea of complex numbers was first introduced by Italian mathematicians in the 16th century.

component. A part; in an *ordered pair,* the object that occurs first is the first component and the object that occurs second is the second component.

$$(2,3)$$ SECOND COMPONENT

FIRST COMPONENT

composite number. A number such as 8, 36 or 100 which is not a *prime number*.

compound condition. Two *simple conditions* combined by a *connective*.

$$X > 3 \quad \wedge \quad X < 5$$

X IS GREATER THAN 3   AND   X IS LESS THAN 5

compound event. In *probability,* more than one, but not all, of the possible events in an occurrence.

compound interest. *Interest* paid not only on the *principal* but also on the interest which has been added to the principal.

compound number. A quantity expressed in more than one unit or denomination, as 2 feet 6 inches.

compound sentence. A sentence constructed from two or more *simple sentences*. For example, $3 + 4 = 7$ or $9 - 6 = 2$. This is a true sentence, because one part of it is true. But if "or" is changed to "and," $3 + 4 = 7$ and $9 - 6 = 2$, then it is a false sentence.

comptometer (kom-tom′e-tur). A trade name for the first successful calculating machine built in 1887 to handle more than one column of digits at a time.

computation. The act or method of carrying out a mathematical process.

computer. An electronic or mechanical device used for solving mathematical problems, for doing clerical work, for figuring probabilities and for running many mechanical operations. There are two basic types:

Analogue computers are used for research problems and to simulate various conditions and circumstances, such as those in space. Every analogue computer is designed for a particular type of problem.

Digital computers make precise calculations on numbers expressed in digits, often using the *binary system*. Numbers represent the elements of a problem, and the answer is given in numbers. Anything that can be counted can be changed into numbers for a digital computer.

Instructions and information for a computer are programmed by specially trained engineers.

Charles Babbage had the first idea for making an automatic digital computer about 1835.

Lord Kelvin had the first idea for an analogue computer in 1876.

Vannevar Bush built the first large analogue computer in 1931.

Howard Aiken built the first electromechanical digital computer in 1944.

John von Neumann did much of the designing in developing today's computers.

concentric circles. Two or more

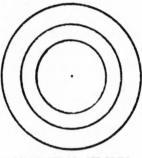

CONCENTRIC CIRCLES

circles in one *plane,* having the same *point* as their center.

concept. A mental impression or an idea and all its associations.

conclusion. The final statement in a *proof,* which follows from previous statements.

concrete number. Belonging to actual objects; opposed to *abstract number.* A number is concrete if it refers to specific objects, such as 2 books.

concurrent lines. Two or more *lines* with a *point* in common.

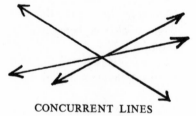

CONCURRENT LINES

condition. See *simple condition, compound condition.*

conditional equation. An *equation* with one or more *variables.* In an equation such as $3x - 1 = 5$, a true statement is formed only if 2 is the replacement for x. 2 is the solution for the equation. The fact that $x = 2$ is the condition that makes the equation true.

Equations that are true for some but not all values of the variable or variables are called conditional equations. $x + y = 7$ is true for a number of pairs of values, but not true for other pairs of values. See *identical equation.*

conditional open sentence (or implication). A sentence formed by joining two sentences in the form "if . . . then." The first sentence is the *hypothesis* (antecedent), and the second sentence is the *conclusion* (consiguent). In the implication, "If $3 + 3 = 6$, then $4 + 3 = 7$," $3 + 3 = 6$ is the hypothesis and $4 + 3 = 7$ is the conclusion. A conditional is usually written in the form: "if p then q," or $p \rightarrow q$. $p \rightarrow q$ is true except where p is true and q is false.

cone. A *solid* bounded by a conical *surface* and a *plane* cutting all elements. If the base is a circle, we call it a circular cone. If the base is perpendicular to its *axis* it is a right circular cone. See *table of formulas p. 213.*

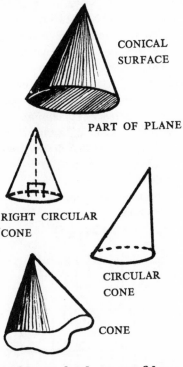

CONICAL SURFACE

PART OF PLANE

RIGHT CIRCULAR CONE

CIRCULAR CONE

CONE

confidence level or confidence coefficient. A term used in testing *hypotheses.* If a 95% confidence level is used, the *probability* of an event occurring by chance is 5 out of 100.

configuration. The way the *elements* in anything are arranged.

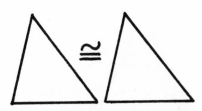

congruent figures. Two or more *plane figures* that have the same size and shape. See also *corresponding angles, sides, vertices.*

congruent numbers. Two numbers which have the same remainder when they are each divided by a third number (called a *modulus*). For example, 7 and 9 are congruent, modulus 2. This is written $7 \equiv 9 \pmod 2$.

conic sections (kon'ik). From ancient times. Curves formed by the intersection of a *plane* and a right circular *cone.* De-

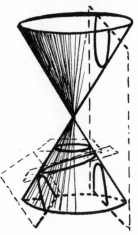

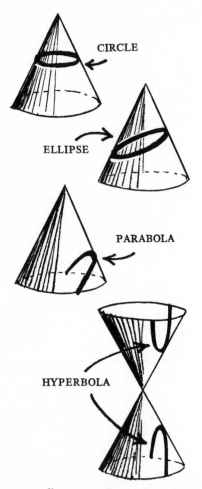

CIRCLE

ELLIPSE

PARABOLA

HYPERBOLA

pending on where the plane cuts through, the conic section may be a *circle,* an *ellipse,* a *parabola* or a *hyperbola.* It may even be a straight line, a pair of straight lines or a point.

conjunction of equations. A *compound sentence* such as $x + y = 7$ and $x - y = 3$. This is true only when $x = 5$ and $y = 2$. See *connective.*

connective. A word or symbol used to combine two or more sentences into one sentence. See *and, or, conditional open sentence.*

consiguent (kon-sihg′you-ent). See *hypothesis, conditional open sentence, conclusion.*

consistent. A set of *assumptions* or *hypotheses* that do not contradict each other.

consistent equations. *Equations* having at least one solution in common.

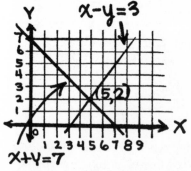

constant. An absolute constant is a number that always has the same value, like the number 10. In $3x^2 + 5$, 5 is a constant. An arbitrary constant has a particular value in a particular problem. Arbitrary constants are usually represented by letters from the beginning of the alphabet—a, b, c, etc. See *variable*.

constant factor. See *geometric progression*.

construction. The drawing of a figure in geometry, usually with *straightedge* and *compass*, to fulfill the conditions that describe it.

contiguous (kon-tihg'you-us). In geometry, next to and touching.

CONTIGUOUS
ANGLES

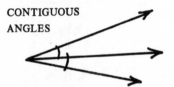

continued fraction. A number plus a fractional number whose *denominator* is a number plus a fractional number, and so on. See *fraction*.

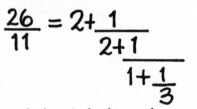

$$\frac{26}{11} = 2 + \cfrac{1}{2 + \cfrac{1}{1 + \cfrac{1}{3}}}$$

continuity. A fundamental concept in algebra, geometry and topology saying there are no

"holes" in a line; the line extends in a continuous fashion with no breaks. See *density*.

continuous. Flowing, without a break. See *discrete*.

continuous curve. A *curve* which is not broken into two or more parts.

continuous data. *Data* obtained from a moving sheet of paper on which a line is drawn to show changes taking place at every moment of time.

continuous numbers. A *set* of *real numbers* that can be put into a *one-to-one correspondence* with every *point* on a *number line*. The *rational numbers* are not continuous.

continuum (kon-tin'you-um). An *infinite set* of numbers or objects between any two other numbers or objects. The set of all *real numbers* is called the continuum of real numbers. Any *closed interval* of real numbers is a continuum. An infinite set of numbers can be inserted between any two numbers, 1 and 2, for example, and there are no gaps in the line.

$$\overset{\displaystyle 1\frac{5}{16}\ \ 1\frac{7}{16}}{\underset{\displaystyle 1\ \ \ \ 1\frac{1}{4}\ \ 1\frac{3}{8}\ 1\frac{1}{2}\ \ \ \ \ \ \ \ \ \ \ \ 2}{\longleftrightarrow}}$$

contour. The outline of any figure or body.

contradiction or **contradictory statement.** Two statements. If one is true, the other is false.

contrapositive. A statement formed by reversing the order and negating the parts of an *"if . . . then"* statement. For example, if 2 sides of a triangle are equal, the angles opposite these sides are equal. If 2 sides of a triangle are not equal, the angles opposite these sides are not equal.

converging lines. *Lines* that meet at a *point.*

CONVERGING LINES

converse of a statement. If a statement says, "If p then q," the converse thus would be, "If q then p." For example, "If the triangle is *isosceles,* it has two equal angles." The converse is, "If the triangle has two equal angles, it is an isosceles triangle."

conversion table. A table comparing units in two different systems. For the conversion table of *metric units into English units,* see *p. 220.*

coordinates (koh-ord'i-nitz). If a number is associated with a *point* on a *line,* the number is

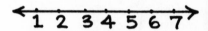

called the coordinate of the point. If an *ordered pair* of numbers is associated with a point on a plane, the numbers are called coordinates of the point. For point P, 3 is the

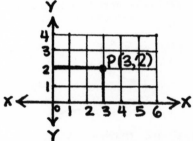

x-coordinate and 2 is the y-coordinate. See *abscissa, ordinate, Cartesian coordinates. Latitude* and *longitude* are co-ordinates used to locate points on the sphere of the earth.

NICHOLAS
COPERNICUS

Copernicus, Nicholas (koh-purr′ nih-kus), 1473–1543. A Polish astronomer, mathematician, doctor and lawyer whose description of our solar system is the basis of modern astronomy. He believed that the sun was the center of the universe and the earth and other planets revolved around it.

coplanar points (ko-plain′ur). *Points* that lie on the same *plane*. A *square* is a *set* of coplanar points.

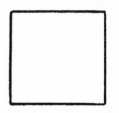

cord. A measure of a volume of wood, 128 cubic feet. See *table p. 217.*

corollary (kar′uh-ler′ee). A *theorem* that follows directly from the *proof* of another theorem.

correction. A quantity or number that must be applied to ensure accuracy in the solution of a problem, such as mapping a course with a marine compass.

correspondence. A one-to-one relationship between sets. Every element in one set can be matched with one and only one element in another set, and every element in the second set can be matched with one and only one element of the first set.

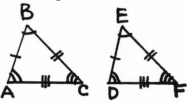

corresponding angles. In *congruent* triangles below, $\angle B$ and $\angle E$, $\angle A$ and $\angle D$, $\angle C$ and $\angle F$ are congruent.

corresponding angles of triangles.
In *congruent* triangles, those angles in the same relative positions.

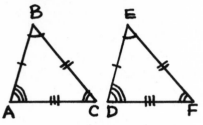

corresponding sides. In two similar or *congruent* triangles, such as the triangles above, $\overline{AB}$ and $\overline{DE}$ are corresponding sides. So are $\overline{BC}$ and $\overline{EF}$ and $\overline{AC}$ and $\overline{DF}$.

corresponding vertices. In the similar or *congruent* triangles above, the *vertices* A and D, B and E, and C and F are corresponding vertices.

cosecant (koh-see′kant).

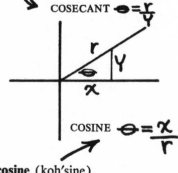

cosine (koh′sine).

cost. The price of something.

cost formula. See *table of formulas p. 215.*

cotangent.

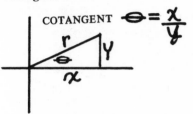

coulomb (koo-lom′). A unit of electrical charge that measures the amount of electricity flowing in one second when the current is one *ampere.*

counterclockwise. In the opposite direction to the way clock hands travel.

counting. *Assigning* to every member of a *set* a number in an ordered *sequence.* The last number assigned is the *cardinal number* of the set.

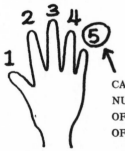

CARDINAL
NUMBER
OF THE SET
OF FINGERS

counting numbers. The set of numbers 1, 2, 3, 4, 5 . . .

counting system. Any system for putting numerals or objects in order, to work with them one at a time.

credit. Power to buy or borrow on trust; the balance in an account.

cross. A symbol for an *operation* on *sets*. A $\times$ B is read "A cross B," or "the *Cartesian product* of A and B."

cryptogram (krypt′oh-gram). Same as *code*.

cube. A *solid*. A physical model of a cube is the outside of a child's block. A cube has 12 equal edges, each edge is perpendicular to its adjoining edges. The 6 faces of a cube are parts of *planes* bounded by squares.

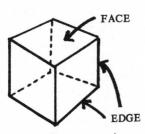

cube. To raise a quantity to the third *power*. 5^3 may be read 5 cubed, or 5 cube or 5 to the third power. 5^3 means $5 \times 5 \times 5$, or 125.

cube problem. The problem of constructing a second cube having twice the volume of a given cube. In the 19th century a solution to the problem with *straightedge* and *compass* was proved impossible.

cube root. The process *inverse* of raising to a *cube*. If $(2)^3 = 8$, then $\sqrt[3]{8} = 2$. In general, for every number a, $\sqrt[3]{a}$ is the number whose cube is a.

$\sqrt[3]{a}$ is positive if a is positive.

$\sqrt[3]{a}$ is negative if a is negative.

$\sqrt[3]{a}$ is zero if a is zero.

cubic centimeter. In the metric system, approximately $\frac{1}{1000}$ of a *liter*.

cubic equations. *Equations* in which the highest sum of *exponents* of the *variables* is 3.

cubic foot. 1728 cubic inches, or 28.3 *liters*.

cubic measure. A measure of *volume*. See *table p. 217*.

cubic yard. 27 cubic feet.

Cuisenaire rods (kweez′in-air). A set of colored rods of different but related lengths to help children learn number concepts and ways to operate on numbers. For example, white is 1 and vermillion, which is twice as long, is 2. Together they are the same length as light green, which is 3.

$$1 + 2 = 3.$$

cup. The symbol for *union* of *sets*. A ∪ B is read, "A cup B," or "the union of A and B." See *join*.

curvature. The rate at which the direction of the curve changes per unit along the curve.

curve. An uninterrupted *set* of *points*. There are open curves and closed curves.

CURVES

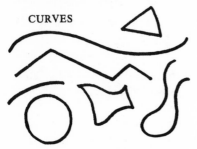

curve of distribution. See *bell-shaped curve*.

curve, simple. A curve that does not cross itself. A simple curve may look more complicated than one that is not simple. It may be open or closed.

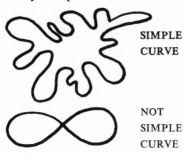

SIMPLE CURVE

NOT SIMPLE CURVE

cybernetics (sy′bur-net′iks). The processes of thinking, problem solving, communications, etc. in people and machines. See *Wiener, Norbert*.

cycle. An interval of time in which some regular event takes place.

cycloid (sy′kloyd). A curve traced by a *point,* as on the rim of a wheel, as it rolls along a straight *line* in one *plane*.

CYCLOID

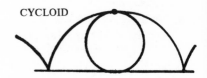

cylinder. A solid. A can is a physical model of a right circular cylinder. It consists of a cylindrical *surface* perpendicular to two parallel *circular closed regions*. The right circular cylinder is the one we usually see in our physical world. However, there are other kinds of cylinders too.

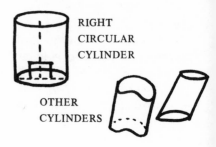

RIGHT CIRCULAR CYLINDER

OTHER CYLINDERS

D

D. D is the Roman numeral for 500.

d. A symbol for *distance* and for *diameter*. It is used in the formula d = rt.

D'Alembert, Jean (dahl-ahm-bayr′), 1717–1783. French mathematician, astronomer and philosopher. He was particularly interested in integral calculus and in Newton's laws of motion. He formulated the D'Alembert test for convergence of an infinite series and the D'Alembert principle, which states that the forces in an object which resist acceleration must be equal and opposite to the forces that produce the acceleration.

data. Facts or information often arranged in charts or graphs to show the relationship between them.

date line, international. An imaginary line on the surface of the earth, running roughly along the 180th meridian. By international agreement, at midnight

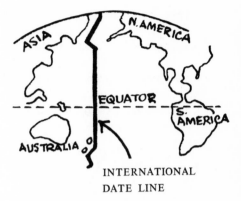

INTERNATIONAL
DATE LINE

along the international date line, a day ends on the eastern side and a new day begins on the western side.

day. The 24-hour period of time it takes the earth to rotate once on its axis.

debenture (deh-ben′tyour). A statement of debt. The value of a debenture bond depends only on the credit of the issuer.

debit. In bookkeeping, the cost of an item, which is marked on an account or ledger sheet as something owed.

deca. Prefix meaning ten.

decade. A period of ten years.

decagon (dehk′uh-gon). A *polygon* having 10 sides.

decagram. 10 *grams* in the metric system. See *table p. 219.*

decahedron. A *polyhedron* with 10 faces or sides.

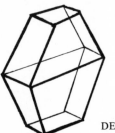

DECAHEDRON

decaliter. 10 *liters* in the metric system.

decameter. 10 *meters* in the metric system.

deci. Prefix meaning one-tenth.

decibel. A unit for measuring the loudness of sound; $\frac{1}{10}$ of a *bel.* A painfully loud sound is about 120 decibels; a barely audible sound is 0 decibels.

decigram. One-tenth of a *gram* in the *metric system.*

deciliter. One-tenth of a *liter* in the *metric system.*

decillion (dih-sill′yun). In the United States and France, the *cardinal number* 1 followed by 33 zeros; in England and Germany, 1 followed by 60 zeros.

decimal equivalent of a fraction. A decimal fraction equal to a *common fraction.* $\frac{3}{4} = .75$.

decimal fraction. A *fractional number* may be expressed in decimal form. Seven-tenths may be $\frac{7}{10}$ or .7. In .7 the denominator is not written but it is understood. The dot in .7 is called a *decimal point.*

.4 is read 4 tenths
.04 is read 4 hundredths

decimal, nonterminating. *Decimal fractions* are often used to approximate the value of *common fractions.*

$$\frac{1}{3} = .3333 \ldots$$

There are two kinds of nonterminating decimals:
In .3333 . . . the digit 3 repeats. It is called a repeating, nonterminating decimal.
A decimal representation for π is 3.14159 . . . This is a nonterminating decimal that does not repeat.

decimal point. A dot or point that separates a *decimal fraction* from the whole numbers. When reading decimal fractions, the decimal point is read as "and." The decimal point was first used in the early 17th century. It is written differently in different countries:

In the U.S., 2.37

In England, 2·37

In France and Germany, 2,37

decimal, terminating. In $\frac{1}{4} = .25$ we sometimes call .25 a *terminating* decimal. However, .25 can be considered .25000 . . . with the 0 repeating. See *decimal, nonterminating.*

decimals, changing to fractional numerals. A decimal numeral such as .6 may be written as a fractional numeral by using the denominator which indicates the place value correctly.

$$.6 = \frac{6}{10}$$

Any *nonterminating, repeating decimal* can be expressed in fractional form. See *fraction.*

decimals, changing to percent. A decimal such as .6 can be expressed as a percent.

$$.6 = 60\%$$
$$.06 = 6\%$$
$$.625 = 62\frac{1}{2}\% \text{ or } 62.5\%$$

decimal system. Any numeration system with a *base* of ten.

decimeter. One-tenth of a *meter* in the *metric system,* or ten *centimeters.* See *table p. 219.*

Dedekind, Richard (ded'ih-kint), 1831–1916. German mathematician, a member of the "German school," which included *Cantor.* He did much work on irrational numbers and infinite classes. He in vented the *infinite* class of algebraic numbers called ideals, and the Dedekind cut in the theory of *irrational numbers.*

deduce. To reach a conclusion based on certain known *data.*

deduct. To take away, or *subtract.*

deduction. A result or conclusion based on a set of statements each of which is justified by a *postulate,* or is given to be true, or is based on a *theorem* previously proved.

deductive reasoning. The method of reasoning whereby a general statement is applied to a particular case. For example:

1. All students must take 2 years of mathematics in order to receive a diploma. (A general statement.)

2. Henry is a student who wishes to receive a diploma. (A specific statement.)

3. He must take 2 years of mathematics. (Conclusion.) See *syllogism.*

deductive system. A set of undefined *terms, definitions, as-*

sumptions or *postulates* are used to deduce *theorems* through the application of the laws of logic.

defective number. A *whole number* in which the sum of its *factors* (except itself) is less than the number itself. 16 is a defective number; its factors, 1, 2, 4 and 8, add up to 15.

deficient number. Same as *defective number.*

deficit. The amount by which a sum (usually money) is short of a required amount.

definition, mathematical. An agreement about the meaning of words and symbols used in mathematics.

degree. In geometry, a degree is a unit of angular measure. A

STRAIGHT ANGLE

RIGHT ANGLE

straight angle is 180°; a right angle is 90°. In temperature measurement, a degree is a unit of temperature. Normal body heat is 98.6°; the freez-

ing point of water is 32° *Fahrenheit.*

Of a *monomial.* The degree of a monomial is the sum of the *exponents* of the *variables.* If there is no variable, the degree is 0.

The degree of 3x is 1.

The degree of $5x^2$ is 2.

The degree of $2x^2y^3$ is 5.

The degree of 4 is 0.

Of a *polynomial.* The degree of the monomial term of highest degree.

The degree of
$$9x^3 + 4x^2 - 7x + 2 \text{ is } 3.$$

degree of an equation. The *degree* of $2a + b = 5$ is an *equation* of the first degree. It is called a linear equation, because its graph is a line. $3x^2 + 5 = 17$ is an equation of the second degree, called a *quadratic equation.* See *analytic geometry.*

degree of an expression. See *degree.*

deka (or deca). Prefix meaning ten.

delta. The fourth letter of the Greek alphabet and their numeral for 4. It was written δ or Δ and called delta. When written Δy, we read it as the difference of the y-coordinates.

deMéré, Antoine Lombard, Chevalier (de-mair-ay), 1610–

1684. A French gambler, friend of *Fermat* and *Pascal*. He asked them to solve this problem mathematically: If a certain number of points were needed to win an unfinished dice game, with one player ahead, how could the stakes be divided fairly?

Solving this problem started Pascal on his famous *probability* research, the result of which was the *Pascal triangle* of probability.

Democritus (dee-mok′rih-tus), 460–370 B.C. Greek scientist and mathematician, known chiefly as the originator of the atomic theory of the structure of the universe. He is supposed to be the first mathematician to state the formula for finding the volume of a cone or a pyramid. His theories foreshadowed the work of *Archimedes* and provided the beginning of infinitesimal calculus.

DeMoivre, Abraham (de-mwa′ vr), 1667–1754. French mathematician, friend of *Newton* and one of the group who investigated the dispute between Newton and *Leibniz*. He worked in trigonometry but is best known for his "Doctrine of Chances," a study of *prob-*

ability. He also helped form the idea of a normal curve of distribution. DeMoivre's theorem is a rule for raising a complex number to a power.

DeMorgan, Augustus, 1806–1871. English mathematician and logician, a noted teacher and founder of the London Mathematical Society. He wrote on probability, trigonometry and paradoxes. DeMorgan's rule is used in set theory.

denominate number. A number that refers to a special unit of measurement: 7 inches, 25 dollars, 19 pounds. A compound denominate number refers to two sets of measurements, such as 6 feet 5 inches.

6 FEET, 5 INCHES

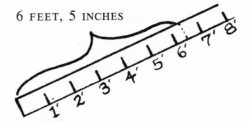

denominator. In ⅖, the 5 is the denominator.

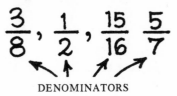

DENOMINATORS

density of matter. A unit volume of mass that shows the number of pounds per cubic feet, or grams per cubic centimeter.

density property. When we say the *set* of *rational numbers* is dense, we mean that it is always possible to find other rational numbers between any two rational numbers.

Between 0 and 1 there is ½. Between 0 and ½ there is ¼, between 0 and ¼ there is ⅛.

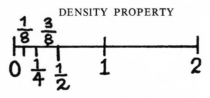

DENSITY PROPERTY

denumerable (dee-noom′uhr-uh-bull). A *set* that can be counted or put into *one-to-one correspondence* with the *natural numbers*.

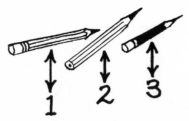

dependent equations. Two *equations* such as $x + y = 3$ and $4x + 4y = 12$ have many common solutions. Any pair of numbers that *satisfies* one equation satisfies the other. Their graphs are the same line. Such equations are called dependent.

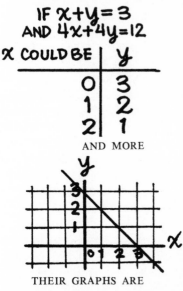

DEPENDENT EQUATIONS

THEIR GRAPHS ARE THE SAME LINE

dependent variable. In the *function* $y = 3x$, the value of y, when $x = 2$, is 6. y is sometimes called the dependent variable. Of course, if $y = 6$, then x is 2. See *function*.

depreciation. Loss in value of goods or property, or a decrease in the value of money.

depressed equation. An *equation* whose *degree* is less than the original equation. It is the result of reducing the number of *roots* of an equation. For example, given $x^2 + 2x - 3 = 0$, if both members are divided by $x - 1$, the result is the depressed equation $x + 3 = 0$.

Desargues, Gérard (duh-sarg'), 1593–1662. French engineer and architect whose theories on conics had a great effect on the work of *Descartes* and *Pascal*. He was one of a new group of mathematicians who realized that Greek geometry could not be pursued much farther, and who looked for new ways of extending the scope of geometry.

RENÉ DESCARTES

Descartes, René (day-kart'), 1596–1650. French mathematician, philosopher and scientist, often called, "the father

of modern mathematics." Descartes' main contribution to mathematics was his invention of *Cartesian* or *analytic geometry,* which united algebra and geometry. This enabled mathematicians to map any equation as a set of points on a *graph*.

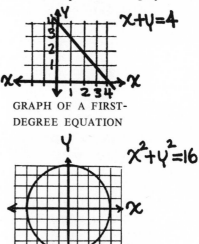

GRAPH OF A FIRST-DEGREE EQUATION

GRAPH OF A SECOND-DEGREE EQUATION

Descartes learned that the graph of a first-degree equation makes a straight line; the graph of a second-degree equation makes a circle and other conic sections and, the higher the degree of the equation, the more complex the curve on the graph. He also demonstrated that if an equation could be graphed as a line, a line could be written as an equation.

Descartes tried to determine how many roots of an equation are positive and how many are negative. A rule for determining the upper limit to the number of positive and negative roots, based upon variations in signs, is called Descartes' rule of signs, although the discovery was actually made by *Harriot*.

descending order. In $3x^4 + 4x^3 - 3x^2 + 2x + 7$, the terms of the *polynomial* are written in descending order. The term with the highest power of the *variable* is first (at the left) and the term with the next highest is second, and so on.

description of a set. A set may be described by listing its members $A = \{1, 2, 3, 4, 5\}$. It may be described by a condition as "the set of natural numbers less than 6."

determinant. A square array of elements that shows the sum of the *products*.

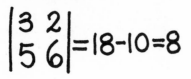

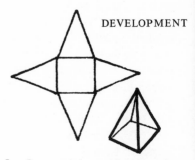

DEVELOPMENT

development (or net). The *plane geometric* figure obtained by opening up and flattening a *solid* figure without changing the area of its surfaces.

deviation from the mean. In statistics, a measure of the variation from the trend. If the mean (average) of a set of numbers is 80 and one *member* of the set is 75, we say that its deviation from the norm is 5.

deviation, standard. A statistic that characterizes a *distribution* of *scores*. See *central tendency*.

diagonal. A *line segment* connecting two nonadjacent *vertices* of a *polygon*.

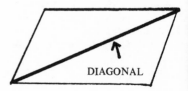

DIAGONAL

diagram. A drawing showing data, geometric figures, etc.

diameter. A *line segment* that contains the center of a circle and whose *endpoints* are on the circle. A *chord* which contains the center of the *circle*. See *table of formulas p. 212.*

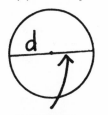

DIAMETER

difference. The amount by which one quantity or number is greater or less than another. The mathematical *operation* for finding differences is *subtraction* and the symbol is a *minus* sign —. See also *absolute difference.*

difference engine. The first machine designed by *Charles Babbage* in 1822. It was actually an adding machine designed to compute and print tables automatically and was accurate to six decimal places. The machine was never completed, though the British government contributed about 17,000 pounds (an enormous sum in those days) toward it because engineering techniques of the time were not advanced enough.

differential calculus. A branch of mathematics that may be applied to such problems as finding the speed of a given object at a given time, or the steepness of a curve at any point. It is also known as the calculus of change, or fluxions. See *Newton, Leibniz.*

digit. The ten digits in our numeration system are 0, 1, 2, 3, 4, 5, 6, 7, 8, 9. The word comes from the Latin "digitus," meaning finger or toe.

digital computer. A device, either mechanical or electrical, for carrying out mathematical operations directly on the information received. The digits are counted rather than being translated into another form as in *analogue computers.* A digital computer has four main parts. The input feeds instructions into the computer. The arithmetic unit carries out the arithmetic operations. The memory unit stores instructions and information for later use. The output receives and transmits the answer. See *computer.*

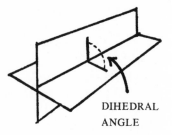

DIHEDRAL
ANGLE

dihedral angle (die-heed'rul).
The *angle* made by two intersecting planes. The two planes
are called the faces and the line
of intersection is called the
edge.

dilation. The property which per-
mits a geometric figure to con-
tract or expand; an *invariant*
property of *Euclidean geometry.*

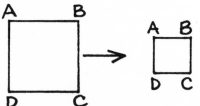

PROPERTIES OF SQUARE
ABCD AND CIRCLE O
ARE THE SAME, EVEN
THOUGH THEIR SIZES
CHANGE.

dime. A United States coin equal
to 10 cents, $\frac{1}{10}$ of a dollar.

dimension. A measure. *Points* are
considered to have no dimension; *line segments* have length,
or one dimension; *plane figures*
have area, or two dimensions;
solids have volume, or three
dimensions.

• NO DIMENSION

length ONE DIMENSION

height TWO DIMENSIONS

length THREE DIMENSIONS

height

width *length*

Diophantus (die-oh-fan'tus), ?–
A.D. 320? A member, along
with Hero and Pappus, of the
Second Alexandrian School.
He wrote 13 books forming the
"Arithmetica," of which 6 sur-
vive. They are the earliest
known works on algebra. His
chief contribution was the introduction of a new notation
using contractions of words or
symbols to stand for unknown
quantities and operations. Until that time the Greeks had
used all the letters of the alphabet for particular numbers,

and had no way to represent unknown quantities.

directed line segment. A *line segment* in which one *endpoint* is designated the initial point and the other endpoint is the terminal point. The segment is directed from the first endpoint to the second.

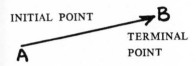

INITIAL POINT   **B**

TERMINAL POINT

A

DIRECTED LINE SEGMENT AB

directed numbers. Signed numbers. Geometrically, numbers are associated with points on a line. Zero is associated with a point, then numbers are associated with the points to the left and right of it. Numbers to the right of the zero point are called *positive numbers,*

-3 -2 -1   0 +1 +2 +3

those to the left are called *negative numbers.* Sometimes, instead of *plus* or *minus* signs, the signed numerals have arrows pointing to the right for positive and to the left for negative.

$$\overset{\leftarrow}{3} \quad \overset{\rightarrow}{5}$$

direct proportion. See *direct variation.*

direct variation. In a set of ordered number pairs $\{(10, 2)$ $(15, 3)$ $(20, 4)\}$, for any value except zero, the quotient of any pair is constant:

$$\frac{10}{2} = 5, \; \frac{15}{3} = 5, \; \frac{20}{4} = 5$$

When the *ratio* is the same for any pair in a set of pairs, the set of pairs is a direct variation.

POSSIBLE PAIRS OF
VALUES FOR Y = 5x

x	y
1	5
2	10
3	15
4	20
5	25

discount. An amount deducted from a bill. The rate of discount is usually given as a percent.

discrete. Separate or distinct. The points on the line associated with the *natural numbers* are discrete. The opposite of discrete is *continuous.*

disjoint sets. The *set* of boys in a class and the set of girls in a

DISJOINT SETS

class are said to be disjoint because there is no member which belongs to both sets.

disjunction. A *compound sentence* formed by joining two *simple statements* with "or" is called a disjunction. "It is raining or the game is being played," is an example of a disjunction. In mathematical statements, the symbol for the disjunction "or" is "$\vee$." $5 < x \vee 5 = x$. For a disjunction to be true, one or both simple statements must be true. See *connective*.

distance. See *table of formulas p. 215.*

distance on a number line. The *absolute value* of the difference between the *coordinates* of any two *points*.

A   B

4 5 6 7 8 9 10

$$AB = |4 - 9| = 5$$
OR
$$AB = |9 - 4| = 5$$

distribution. In statistics, an arrangement of a set of values. The picture shows a *frequency* distribution.

MARKS	FREQUENCY
90–100	III
80–90	HHT I
70–80	IIII
60–70	II

Binomial distribution is used in *probability*. See *binomial theorem.*

distribution curve (frequency curve). In statistics, the graph made from a frequency distribution. A normal distribution curve is usually *bell-shaped* or onion-shaped, with the greatest

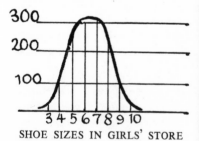

SHOE SIZES IN GIRLS' STORE

number of scores clustering near the middle of the curve. If the distribution or *frequency curve* is "off center," for example, as in one showing ages at which people marry, it is called a *skewed curve*.

distributive property of multiplication over addition. In the *real number* system, this is a link between the operation of addition and multiplication. In $2 \times 14 = 28$, 2 and 14 are *factors* and 28 is their *product*. 14 may be renamed $10 + 4$. $2 \times (10 + 4)$ is the same as $2 \times 10 + 2 \times 4$. In general, for numbers a, b and c, this property is written $a(b + c) = ab + bc$. For example, $2 \times (4 + 5) = 2 \times 4 + 2 \times 5$, or 18.

A *factor* can be written as the sum of two addends.

A FACTOR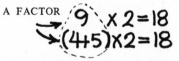

dividend. In the operation of division, the number that is to be divided by another number. A

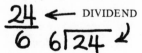

dividend is also a sum of money paid to stockholders of a company from earnings, or to insured persons from the profits of an insurance company.

divisible. When a number is divided by another number so that the remainder is zero, the first number is said to be divisible by the second. For example, 12 is divisible by 6, by 4, by 3 and by 2.

divisibility, tests for.

A number is divisible by 2 if the end digit on the right side is 0, 2, 4, 6 or 8.

A number is divisible by 3 if the sum of the value of all the digits in the numeral is divisible by 3.

A number is divisible by 4 if the value of the last two right-hand digits is divisible by 4.

A number is divisible by 5 if it ends in 5 or 0.

A number is divisible by 6 if it is even and if the sum of the value of its digits is divisible by 3.

A number is usually divisible by 8 if the sum of the value of its last three digits is divisible by 8, or if the last three digits are zeros.

A number is divisible by 9 if the sum of the value of its digits is divisible by 9.

division. An *operation* on numbers, the *inverse* of multiplication. For example, $18 \div 2 = 9$ means $9 \times 2 = 18$. If one factor is unknown, as in $\square \times 2 = 18$, the factor may be found as $\frac{18}{2}$ or 9. In general, $a \div b = c$ means $c \times b = a$. Division by zero is meaningless. $\frac{6}{0}$ is meaningless.

$$\frac{6}{0} = ? \quad \frac{10}{1} = 10 \quad \frac{0}{6} = 0$$

division property of equality. If both members of an *equation* are divided by the same number (other than zero), the resulting equation is *equivalent* to the original one. In general, if $a = b$ then $\frac{a}{c} = \frac{b}{c}$.

$$\frac{9x}{9} = \frac{18}{9}$$
$$x = 2$$
$$9x = 18$$
$$9 \cdot 2 = 18 \quad true$$

divisor. The number by which the *dividend* is to be divided.

DIVIDEND → $\dfrac{24}{6} = 4$ ← QUOTIENT

DIVISOR →

divisor, common (or *common factor*). A common divisor of 18

and 27 is 3. But the *greatest common divisor* or factor of these numbers is 9.

dodecagon (doh-dek'a-gon). A *polygon* having 12 sides.

dodecahedron. A *polyhedron* having 12 faces. In ancient times it was the symbol of the universe.

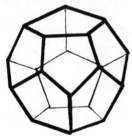

Dodgson, Charles. See *Carroll, Lewis*.

dollar. The basic money unit of the United States, equal to 100 cents.

domain of a relation. A relation is a set of *ordered pairs*. The domain is the set of first members of those ordered pairs. The *range* is the set of second members of the ordered pairs of a relation. See *function*.

$$A = \{(1,2),(3,4),(5,6),(7,8)\}$$
$$\text{DOMAIN} = \{1,3,5,7\}$$
$$\text{RANGE} = \{2,4,6,8\}$$

domain of a variable. The set of all possible replacements for a *variable*. The domain may be a *finite set* or an *infinite set*.

double. Twice as much.

double-entry bookkeeping. A method of recording business transactions by making each entry twice, once to the credit of one account and once to the debit of another.

dozen (abbreviation, doz.). 12 units, as a dozen eggs.

dram. 60 grains or $\frac{1}{8}$ oz. in *apothecaries' weight*. See *table p. 216.*

dry measure. Part of the *avoirdupois system,* used to measure such things as fruit and grain. See *table p. 218.*

duodecimal numeration system (doo-oh-des'ih-mul). A system with a *base* of twelve. (Our *decimal system* has a base of ten.) A base twelve system would need two new basic symbols. Some people believe the duodecimal system superior to a base ten system because 12 is divisible by 2, 3, 4 and 6.

0,1,2,3,4,5,6,7,8,9

0,1,2,3,4,5,6,7,8,9,Ↄ,Ɫ

A BASE TWELVE SYSTEM WOULD NEED TWO NEW NUMERALS

duplication of the cube. See *cube problem.*

ALBRECHT DÜRER

Dürer, Albrecht (dyour'er), 1471–1528. A German artist and mathematician. His chief mathematical work, discussing perspective and geometry, appeared in 1525. One of his most famous engravings, "Melancholia," contains a *magic square* that has been copied often. He also gave a construction which is a very good approximation for the *trisection* of an angle, using only *Euclidean tools.*

dyadic notation (dy-add'ik). See *binary system.*

dyne. A small unit of force which, acting on a mass of 1 gram, gives it an acceleration of 1 centimeter per second.

E

E. E is the abbreviation for energy.

E = mc² is the *Einstein* theory of relativity.

e. A symbol for a *transcendental number*. The value of e is approximately 2.7182818 . . .

It is used as the base of natural *logarithms*. See *Napier*.

edge. The straight *line segment* which is the intersection of two plane *faces* of a *solid,* as the edges of a *cube.*

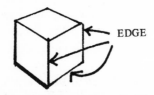

EDGE

Egyptians, mathematics of. The Egyptians were good mathematicians 5,000 years ago. We think they knew how to form right triangles by using a knot-

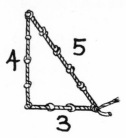

ted rope. Their numeration system looked like this:

The Egyptians were practical mathematicians. They used their mathematics for measuring land, building magnificent buildings that are still standing and for studying the stars in order to calculate the seasons.

ALBERT
EINSTEIN

Einstein, Albert (ine′stine), 1879–1955, was one of the greatest scientists of all time. Born in Germany, he became a Swiss, then later an American citizen. In 1905 he advanced his special theory of relativity. By 1916, he had included other concepts to formulate his general theory of relativity. He revolutionized scientific thinking with his ideas about time, space, mass, light, motion and gravitation, and was one of the founders of the atomic age.

Einstein's renowned equation, $E = mc^2$, stated that matter and energy are interchangeable. $E = mc^2$ means Energy = mass (or matter) $\times$ the velocity of light, squared.

Einstein contributed to the proof of the quantum theory in his work with light. He worked to prove his unified field theory, which combined gravitational and electromagnetic equations in a single theory, until the end of his life.

Einstein theory. Albert Einstein's special and general theory of relativity. See above.

element. A *member* of a *set* or collection.

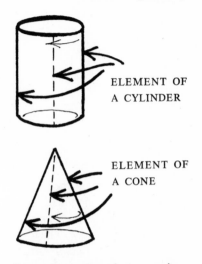

ELEMENT OF
A CYLINDER

ELEMENT OF
A CONE

In geometry, imagine a moving line segment which *generates* a conical or a cylindrical surface. The line segment at any position is called an element.

elementary algebra. See *algebra*.

Elements, The. *Euclid*'s most famous work, consisting of 13 books, that organized what was known about geometry until his time, and which also contained chapters on geometrical algebra and number theory. For more than 2000 years, translations of some books of The Elements were used as school textbooks.

elements of geometry. The fundamental *assumptions* and *undefined terms*. See *Euclid*.

$$SET\ A = \{2, 4, 6, 8\}$$

ELEMENTS OF THE SET

elevation, angle of. ∠ ABC in the diagram.

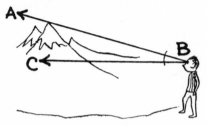

ellipse. (uh-lips′). A geometrical figure like a flattened circle. One of the *conic sections,* an ellipse has two *focii.* The longer segment that passes through the focii is called the *major axis.* The minor axis is a line segment at right angles to the major axis. See *table of formulas p. 212.*

ELLIPSE

MAJOR AXIS   MINOR AXIS

FOCII

elliptical geometry (ee-lip′tik-ul). A branch of *non-Euclidean geometry.*

empty set. One with no elements, written { } or φ. A *set* of this kind would be a set of the people now living who are over 20 feet tall.

enclose. To put inside, usually in *brackets* or *parentheses,* to show that an operation should be performed first or that the quantity enclosed should be thought of as one number.

$$3 \times 4 + 2 \text{ MEANS } (3 \times 4) + 2$$

endpoints. Points at the ends of a *line segment.*

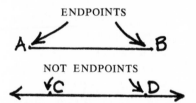

ENDPOINTS

NOT ENDPOINTS

epsilon (eps′ih-lahn). The fifth letter of the Greek alphabet, written E or ϵ and used by the Greeks as their numeral 5. In *set notation,* ϵ indicates an element belonging to a *set.* For example, a ϵ A means that a is an element of set A.

equality. The idea expressed by the equal sign, written =. In $4 + 3 = 7$, "4 + 3" and "7" name the same number. Three

properties of equality are:
1. Equality is *reflexive,* a = a.
2. Equality is *symmetric*. If a = b, b = a.
3. Equality is *transitive*. If a = b and b = c, then a = c.

equal sets. Two sets with exactly the same *elements,* regardless of the order in which the elements appear.

If set A = {0, 1, 2, 3} and
B = {1, 2, 0, 3}, then
A = B.

equal sign. See *equality.*

equation. A *mathematical sentence* with an = sign between two expressions which name the same number. $6 + x = 10$ is an equation. So are $3 + 4 = 7$ and $a + b = b + a$.

equation, members of an. The *expressions* in an equation on either side of the = sign. See *linear equation, quadratic equation.*

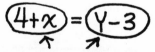

MEMBERS OF
THE EQUATION

equation, roots of an. The values of a *variable* which change the equation into a true statement are called the *roots* or *solutions* of the equation. A root

of $6 + x = 10$ is 4 because $6 + 4 = 10$ is a true statement. The *solution set* of an equation contains all the roots of the equation and no other numbers.

equator. The imaginary *great circle* of the earth or any celestial body *perpendicular* to the axis of its rotation.

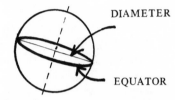

DIAMETER

EQUATOR

equiangular. A *polygon* whose angles have the same measure. An *equilateral triangle* is equiangular.

equidistant. Points that are the same distance from a point of reference.

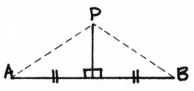

A AND B ARE EQUI-
DISTANT FROM POINT P

equilateral triangle. A triangle with three sides of the same length.

equity. The value or amount of property, above any charges against it.

equivalent. Having the same value.

equivalent equations. Two or more *equations* are equivalent or equal if they have the same *solution set.* $7x - 2 = 19$, $7x = 21$ and $x = 3$ are equivalent equations. The solution in each case is 3.

equivalent sets. Two *sets* are equivalent if they can be placed in *one-to-one correspondence.* For example, there is a one-to-one correspondence between the 26 letters of the alphabet and the whole numbers 1–26.

$$\{ A, B, C, D \ldots Z \}$$
$$\{ 1, 2, 3, 4 \ldots 26 \}$$

Eratosthenes (eh-ra-tos'then-eez), 275–195 B.C. A Greek scholar, head of the library at Alexandria. He wrote on mathematics, astronomy, geography, philosophy and the arts. He devised the *sieve of Eratosthenes,* a way of finding *prime numbers.* He evolved a system of chronology, drew a map of the known world and made a measurement of the circumference of the earth.

erg. A unit of work, equal to one *dyne* of force acting through one *centimeter* of distance.

error. Usually used in *statistics* to show the difference between the true value of a quantity and an uncontrolled variation, such as sampling errors.

error of measurement. The difference between *true length* and *measured length,* because no measurement is exact.

estimate. See *approximate.*

Euclid, about 300 B.C. A Greek

EUCLID

mathematician famous for his *Elements,* a collection of theorems and problems that forms a logical system of geometry. Euclid also wrote on conic sections, optics, algebra and numbers. He proved that the number of primes is infinite. He founded the first school of mathematics at Alexandria. For more than 2,000 years, Euclidean geometry was the only kind taught in schools.

Euclidean algorithm (you-klid′ ee-un). A method for finding the *greatest common factor* of two numbers. The larger number is divided by the smaller one, and the division is repeated, using the remainder as the divisor, until the remainder is zero.

Euclidean construction. A geometric construction made with *compass* and *straightedge*.

EUCLIDEAN CONSTRUCTION
OF A SQUARE

Euclidean geometry. The geometry based on Euclid's *axioms.* See *geometry*.

Euclidean plane. The *set* of all points in the shape of a flat surface. The *plane* extends *infinitely* in all directions, and so has no dimensions. It is a *subset* of all the points in space.

Euclidean tools. *Compass* and *straightedge*.

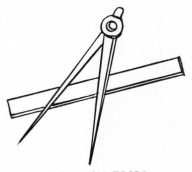

EUCLIDEAN TOOLS

Euclid's 5th or parallel postulate. Through a given *point* outside a straight *line,* one and only one straight line may be drawn that is *parallel* to the given line. Questioning this assumption led to *non-Euclidean geometry*.

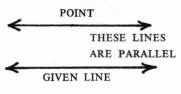

POINT

THESE LINES
ARE PARALLEL

GIVEN LINE

Eudoxus (you-dox'us), about 408–355 B.C. A Greek astronomer, mathematician and physician. He calculated the length of the solar year and is supposed to have formulated some parts of the geometry used in Euclid's works. He was the first Greek astronomer to explain the movements of the planets in a scientific manner.

LEONHARD
EULER

Euler, Leonhard (oi'ler), 1707–1783. Swiss mathematician and a founder of higher mathematics. He is especially known for his work on the calculus of variations. He has been called the father of *topology,* and the Eulerian equation and *Euler's formula* are named for him.

Euler circles. The technique created by Euler to represent statements in logic, geometry and algebra by circles. See *Venn diagrams.*

Euler's formula. In *space geometry,* the formula states that the sum of the number of *vertices* and *faces* of a solid is 2 more than the number of edges: $V + F = E + 2$, where V represents the number of vertices, F the number of faces and E the number of edges.

CUBE

evaluate. To find the value of. To evaluate $x^3 - 2y + z$, if $x = 2$, $y = 3$, $z = 5$, the numerical value of the expression is:

$$(2^3) - 2 (3) + 5$$
$$8 \quad - \quad 6 \; + 5$$
$$2 \; + 5, \text{ or } 7$$

even number. A number that has 2 as one of its *factors.* If x is an integer, then any even number can be written in the form 2x.

event. In *statistics,* the tossing of a coin is a *simple event.* It is also a *subset* of a *sample space.* See *compound event, inde-*

pendent event, mutually exclusive event.

evolution. Finding the *root* of a number; the *inverse* of raising to a power. See *involution.*

exact. In arithmetic, exact usually refers to division where the remainder is zero. 5 is an exact divisor of 15.

See *approximate; measurement, error of; rounded number.*

excessive number. See *abundant number.*

existential quantifier. In *logic* and *algebra,* a symbol that means "some." The word "some" means "at least one." The symbol is $\exists$ and can be written $\exists$ (x)$\{2x + 5 = 8\}$. This can be read, "For some x's, $2x + 5 = 8$."

expanded notation. A way of writing numerals.

$3333 = (3 \times 10 \times 10 \times 10) + (3 \times 10 \times 10) + (3 \times 10) + (3 \times 1)$

3333 is also written in expanded notation as $3 \times 10^3 + 3 \times 10^2 + 3 \times 10 + 3$.

expanded numeral. A numeral written in *expanded notation.*
$200 = (2 \times 10 \times 10)$.

expansion, binomial. The expansion carried out in terms of the *binomial theorem.* $(x + y)^2 =$

$x^2 + 2xy + y^2$.

expansion of an expression. The product of two or more *polynomials;* the reverse of finding the *factors* of an algebraic expression.

exponent. A short way of writing 10×10 is 10^2. The 2 is called the exponent. 10 is the *base.* The exponent 2 tells us how many times 10 is used as a *factor.* a^3 means $a \times a \times a$.
10^6 means $10 \times 10 \times 10 \times 10 \times 10 \times 10$.
y^n means $y \times y \times y \times y \ldots$ n times.

expression. A general term for *numerals,* numerals with signs of *operation, variables* and combinations of these.
5, $2 + 6$, x, 5n, $3n^2 + 6$ and $2(x + 3)$ are all expressions. See *algebraic expression, equivalent.*

exterior angle. An angle formed by lengthening one side of a *polygon* to form a side of the angle and using the *adjacent* side of the polygon as the other side of the angle.

EXTERIOR ANGLE

When lines are cut by a *transversal,* the angles 1, 2, 3 and 4 in the diagram are exterior angles.

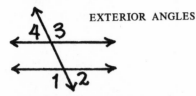

EXTERIOR ANGLES

extracting a square root (or finding a root). To find a square root of a number such as 25 means finding a number which, when raised to the *second power* (or multiplied by itself), gives 25. Since $25 = 5^2$, 5 is a square root of 25. We write $\sqrt{25} = 5$.

extraneous roots. In the algebraic process used in solving *equations,* a number obtained that is not a *root* of the original equation. Extraneous roots are not correct solutions for the original equation.

extremes. In a *proportion,* the first and fourth *terms.* If $2:3 = 6:9$, then the numbers 2 and 9 are the extremes. See *means.*

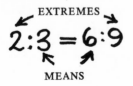

EXTREMES

$$2:3 = 6:9$$

MEANS

F

F. F is the abbreviation for *Fahrenheit.*

f. Used to designate a *function.* f(x) designates the number or value of the function at the number x. For example, if $f(x) = 2x + 1$, then at $x = 1$, $f(1) = 2(1) + 1$ or 3.

face. A polyhedron, such as a *cube* or a *prism,* is a solid formed by parts of planes, which are called faces of the solid. A cube has 6 faces.

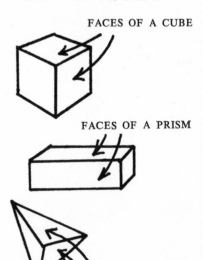

FACES OF A CUBE

FACES OF A PRISM

FACES OF A PYRAMID

factor. In $2 \times 4 = 8$, the 2 and the 4 are called factors of 8. This means that 8 is *divisible* by 2 and 4. If you take the number 36, its factors are 1, 2, 3, 4, 6, 9, 12, 18 and 36. It is divisible by all of these numbers.

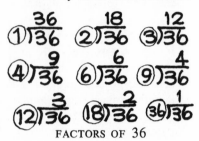

FACTORS OF 36

In algebra, 3 and x are factors of 3x. $x - y$ and $x + y$ are factors of $x^2 - y^2$ because $(x + y)(x - y) = x^2 - y^2$. See *common factor, greatest common factor, prime factor*.

factorial. The factorial of a *natural number* is the *product* of that number and all the natural numbers less than it.
The factorial of the natural number 4 is
$4 \times 3 \times 2 \times 1 = 24$.
4 factorial is written 4!
$3! = 3 \times 2 \times 1 = 6$.

factorization, unique. A theorem stating that any *natural number* can be expressed as a product of one and only one set of *prime numbers*. 6 can be expressed as the product of the primes 2 and 3. $2 \times 3 = 6$.

factor theorem. If an *equation* such as $x^2 - 3x + 2 = 0$ has a *root* or solution of 1, then $(x - 1)$ is a factor of $x^2 - 3x + 2$.

factor tree. A diagram that shows the factors of a given number. The factor tree for 18 looks like this:

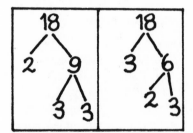

Fahrenheit. A scale for measuring temperature in which the melting point of ice is 32° above 0 and the boiling point of water is 212° above 0.

family of lines. A set of lines whose *equations* can be obtained by varying one *element* of a given equation. For example, if $y = 2x + b$, we can obtain a family of parallel lines by allowing b to take on values of integers.

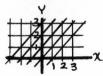

A FAMILY OF LINES

fathom. A nautical measure for water depth, equal to 6 feet.

PIERRE DE FERMAT

Fermat, Pierre de (fair-ma'), 1601–1665. Probably the greatest French mathematician of the 17th century. He was a founder of the modern theory of numbers and independently formulated the basis of *analytic geometry*.

Fermat conjecture. Fermat conjectured that the *terms* in a *sequence* of numbers having the form $2^{2^n} + 1$ are *prime numbers*. *Euler* proved this conjecture incorrect.

Fermat number. A number in the form of $2^{2^n} + 1$, where n is a *positive integer*. The first five numbers in this sequence are:

$$5; 17; 257; 65,537; 4,294,967,297$$

Fermat's last theorem. $x^n + y^n = 2^n$, where n is an *integer* greater than 2, has no solution in *positive integers*. This has never been proved or disproved.

Ferro, Scipio (fehr'ro), 1462–1526. An Italian mathematician who found a solution to the *cubic equation* $x^3 + mx = n$, which he might have read in an Arab work. Because mathematical discoveries were kept secret, his solution was unknown until an argument arose between *Tartaglia* and *Cardan* 30 years later.

Fibonacci numbers (fi-bo-nach' ee). A *sequence* of numbers, each one being the sum of the two numbers before it. These numbers form a pattern not only in mathematics but in nature. The sequence starts like this: 1, 1, 2, 3, 5, 8, 13, 21, 34, 55, 89, 144 . . . See *Leonardo of Pisa*.

field. A mathematical system which consists of a *set* of *elements,* two *operations* and the 11 *arithmetic laws*.

fifteen puzzle. Invented by Sam Lloyd, a box with movable numbers which can be moved to about 10 trillion positions, but which have about 10 trillion others to which they can-

1	2	3	4
5	6	7	8
9	10	11	12
13	14	15	

not be moved. About 100 years ago, the puzzle was played all over Europe for large stakes.

figure. Any *set* of *points* such as *lines, polygons* and *circles.* In *plane geometry,* a figure is a set of points on a plane; in *space geometry* a figure is a set of points in space.

PLANE FIGURES

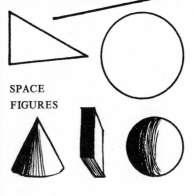

SPACE
FIGURES

figuring. See *computing.*

finger computing. A method of using fingers to do arithmetic operations. Multiplication of numbers over 5 is done this way: To multiply 9×8, on one hand raise four fingers to represent the difference between 9 and the number of fingers on the hand. On the other hand, raise three fingers to show the difference between the second number, (8) and the fingers (5) on that hand.

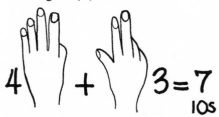

The total number of fingers raised (7) is the number of tens in the product. Then the number of closed fingers on one hand (1) is multiplied by the number closed on the other hand (2), to get the number of ones. $1 \times 2 = 2$, $70 + 2 = 72$.

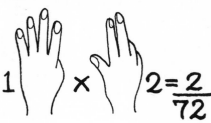

finger symbolism. Most numeration systems are based on either 5, the number of fingers on one hand, or 10, the number on both hands. In some parts of the world, 5 is still represented by an open hand. The Roman symbol V probably started as the symbol for a hand.

finite. Capable of being completely counted; having bounds or limits; the opposite of *infinite*. The set of *natural numbers* from 1 to 10 is a finite set.

finite arithmetic. See *modular arithmetic*.

finite set. A *set* that contains a *finite* or definite number of *elements*. {2, 4, 6, 8, 10} is a finite set of numbers.

five. The name for a number of

5 TREES   5TH TREE

units whose symbol is 5. Five is a *cardinal number*. Its *ordinal number* is fifth.

fluid measure. A measure of the volume of liquids. See *table p. 218.*

focus (pl. foci). See *circle, ellipse.*

FOCUS

foot. A unit of length; 12 inches, ⅓ of a yard, approximately 30.48 centimeters in the metric system. See *table p. 216.*

foot-candle. A measure of the brightness of light on a surface.

foot-pound. A measure of the unit of work. It is equal to a force of 1 pound moving through a distance of 1 foot.

force. Push or pull applied to a body that changes its form or velocity.

force, component of. If we represent a force in a definite direction by *vector* a, we can replace the force with two other forces, b and c. b and c are component forces of a.

The triangle we get is called the triangle of force.

Two or more forces, f_1 and f_2, acting on a body, may be replaced by a simple *vector resultant* force R, forming a parallelogram of forces. Com-

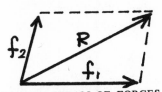

PARALLELOGRAM OF FORCES

ponents of force are used to analyze the forces in terrestrial and celestial mechanics, the movement of the earth and the heavenly bodies.

form. An expression of a certain type. The *standard form* of a numeral, such as 347, names the same number as the *expanded form* $300 + 40 + 7$.

The standard form of a linear *equation* is $ax + by + c = 0$. Form is also a way of stating a principle: $a + b = b + a$ is the generalized form showing the *commutative law*.

The form of an even number can be shown, 2x.

formula. A rule expressed as an *equation*.

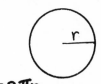

$C = 2\pi r$ IS THE FORMULA FOR FINDING THE CIRCUMFERENCE OF A CIRCLE

four-color map problem. Can a *plane* map showing countries with common boundaries be colored with only 4 colors? If two countries have a common boundary they must be colored with different colors. No one has ever produced a map that required 5 colors. But no one has yet proved mathematically that 4 colors are sufficient.

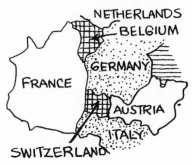

fraction. Sometimes "fraction" is used to mean a number or a fractional number. Sometimes "fraction" is used to name a fractional numeral. The fraction $\frac{3}{4}$ may be used to show

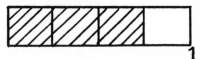

part of a whole. It may indicate division, $3 \div 4$. It may show a ratio of 3 to 4. In $\frac{3}{4}$, 3 is the *numerator* and 4 is the *denominator*.

Fractions may have a value less than 1 ($\frac{3}{4}$), equal to 1 ($\frac{4}{4}$) or greater than 1 ($\frac{5}{4}$). Fractions such as $\frac{3}{4}$ and $\frac{6}{8}$ are *equivalent* fractions.

A fraction such as $\frac{5}{8}$ is said to be in simplest form, or lowest terms, because the numerator and the denominator have no *common factor* except 1.

An expression such as $1\frac{1}{2}$ is called a mixed numeral.

See also *continued fraction, decimal fraction, rational number*.

frame. In some texts, a square is used in a number sentence to

$$15-5 = \square$$

10 IS A SOLUTION

hold the place for the *numeral,* which is the solution to the *open sentence.*

Frege, Gottlob (fray'guh), 1848–1925. German logician who worked on such basic number ideas as: What is zero? What is number?

frequency. In *statistics,* the number of times an *event* occurs.

frequency array. An arrangement of *data* according to the number of times an event occurs. The data may be shown by a graph or in a column of figures.

frequency distribution. A table showing how often each score, event or measurement occurred.

frequency polygon. A *broken-line graph* showing the distribution of collected *data*.

frustum (frus'tum). See *pyramid, truncated*.

function. A special set of *ordered pairs*. This table contains a set of ordered pairs $\{(0,0), (1, 2), (2,4), (3,6), (4,8)\}$. The set of numbers $\{0, 1, 2,$

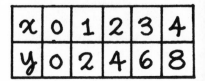

DOMAIN $\{0,1,2,3,4\}$

RANGE $\{0,2,4,6,8\}$

3, 4} is called the *domain* of the set of ordered pairs. The set {0, 2, 4, 6, 8} is the *range*. If each member of the domain is paired with one and only one member of the range, the set of ordered number pairs is called a function. To show or describe a function we may write y = 2x; x is a member of the *natural numbers*.

fundamental operations. See *operations*.

fundamental principle of arrangements. If a man can travel from New York to Chicago in 3 ways and from Chicago to San Francisco in 4 ways, then he can go from New York to San Francisco in 3 × 4 or 12 ways. If a thing can be done in x ways, and a second thing can be done in y ways, then the total number of ways for doing the two things in succession is x times y ways.

SAN FRANCISCO

CHICAGO

NEW YORK

fundamental theorem of arithmetic. Every integer greater than 1 can be written as a product of *primes*. For example, $8 = 2 \times 2 \times 2$. $7 = 7 \times 1$. Every prime, like 7 or 11, is its own product of primes.

G

g. Abbreviation for *gravity,* or a unit of the force of gravity. The force of gravity at the earth's surface is 1g.

GALILEO
GALILEI

Galilei, Galileo (gal-ih-lay′ee), 1564–1642. A great Italian astronomer, mathematician and physicist who laid the foundations for modern experimental science. His construction of an astronomical telescope enlarged man's idea of the universe. He formulated many physical laws mathematically, including the first new laws of bodies in motion since Aristotle's. He disproved Aristotle's theory that heavier bodies fall faster than light ones, and developed the formula $d = 16t^2$ for freely falling bodies. He was tried by the Inquisition for supporting the *Copernican* theory of the solar system.

gallon. A unit of *liquid measure,* equal to 4 quarts or 231 cubic inches. See *table p. 218.*

EVARISTE
GALOIS

Galois, Evariste (gal-wah′), 1811–1832. A French mathematician who by the time he was 17 had evolved original concepts on the theory of algebra and had made important contributions to the theories of numbers, equations and functions. He helped to formulate the theory of groups in algebra. At 21, he was killed in a duel.

SIR FRANCIS
GALTON

Galton, Sir Francis, 1822–1911. An English statistician and sociologist, and a cousin of Charles Darwin. His chief studies related to the laws of heredity. He greatly influenced the introduction of statistics to anthropologists and biologists in the United States.

game theory. Sometimes called "Monte Carlo methods." A branch of mathematics concerned, among other things, with *probability*. The term was first used by *von Neumann* in 1928 to describe the strategy of winning at poker. It was later enlarged to include subjects from military tactics to criminal detection. Computers may eventually make it possible to solve similar problems in every field of human endeavor by the use of mathematics.

gamma (gam′ma). The third letter of the Greek alphabet, used for

the numeral 3, and written Γ
or γ. It may be used to designate an *interior angle* of a
triangle.

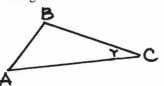

Gauss, Karl Friedrich (gous),
1777–1855. German mathe-
matician and astronomer, considered one of the most original
mathematicians who ever lived.
He completed his first major
work at 19, and was famous
for his contributions to number theory, geometry and
astronomy. He was the first to
prove the fundamental theory
of algebra and was a pioneer
in *non-Euclidean geometry,
statistics* and *probability,* the
theory of functions and the
geometry of curved surfaces.
He invented a telegraph, and
made a surveyor's instrument.

CARL
FRIEDRICH
GAUSS

gauss. Named after Karl Gauss.
A unit to measure the strength
of a magnetic field.

generalized form, in writing equations or terms. See *form.*

generate. In mathematics, to trace
out. Line AB, moving parallel
to line CD, generates a *surface.*

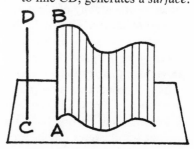

The moving line AB is called
a generatrix. To generate also
means to form the *positive
integers* after number one. For
example, $1 = 1$, $2 = 1 + 1$,
$3 = 2 + 1 = 1 + 1 + 1$. Each
larger integer is generated by
adding one to the previous integer.

geodesic (jee-oh-deh'sick). The
shortest line segment between
two points in space.

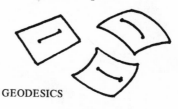

GEODESICS

geodesy (jee-od'eh-see). A branch of applied mathematics in which, by observation and measurement, the exact position of points, shapes and areas of the earth's surface are determined. It is also used to determine the shape, size, curve and gravity of the earth.

geometric means. The *terms* between two given terms in a *geometric progression.*

geometric progression, or geometric sequence. A *sequence* in which the *ratio* of each term and the one before it is the same throughout. In the progression 2, 6, 18, 54, each one is 3 times greater than the one before it. The constant factor is sometimes called the *common ratio* of the progression.

geometry. The branch of mathematics that deals with the relationships, properties and measurements of *solids, surfaces, lines* and *angles*. It also considers spatial relationships, the theory of *space* and *figures* in space. The name comes from Greek words meaning "land" and "to measure." Geometry was first used by the Egyptians to measure land and was later highly developed by the great Greek mathematicians. After *Euclid* organized all the geometry known to his time, very little was added until *Descartes* invented *analytic geometry* in 1637. In the 19th century, new kinds of geometry, called *non-Euclidean* geometries, were created. Five kinds of geometry, classified by *Klein,* are Euclidean, affine, projective, topology and point-set.

geometry, analytic. A geometry that unifies algebra and geometry. Numbers of algebra are attached to the points of geometry. Many kinds of lines, curves and surfaces then may be examined by means of mathematical *equations.* These

ANY EQUATION CAN BE
PICTURED IN A GRAPH

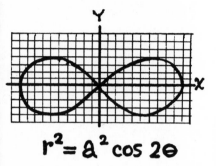

$$r^2 = a^2 \cos 2\theta$$

equations are pictured in the form of graphs. *René Descartes* and *Fermat* were the founders of analytic geometry.

geometry, Euclidean. The geometry based on the *assumptions* of *Euclid* and dealing with the study of *plane* and *solid* or *space geometry*.

geometry, non-Euclidean. Any geometry not based upon Euclid's assumptions; in particular, the substitution of a postulate different from *Euclid's parallel postulate,* which said that one and only one line can be drawn through a point outside a line and parallel to the line. Until the 19th century, this was accepted as a "self-evident truth." The replacement of this postulate and the development of new geometries led to a new look at the basic assumptions on which mathematics is built. If we assume that 2 or more lines can be drawn through point P and always intersect, we have a non-Euclidean geometry called spherical geometry.

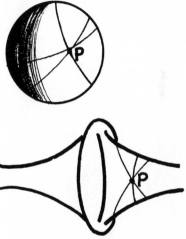

If we assume that 2 or more lines can be drawn through point P and not intersect the original line, we have pseudo-spherical geometry. The founders of non-Euclidean geometry were *Gauss, Riemann, Bolyai* and *Lobachevski,* all of whom investigated the possibilities of changing Euclid's assumption about parallel lines.

See *affine, point-set, topology.*

geometry, nonmetric. "No measurement" geometry.

geometry, plane. Deals with *points, line segments* and *figures* on a plane surface.

geometry, projective. Deals with *properties* and spatial relations of figures as they are projected.

geometry, solid. Now usually called *space geometry.*

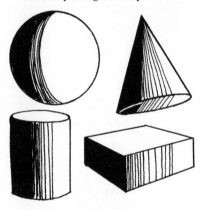

geometry, space. The study of a *set* of *points*. Sometimes the term is used for solid geometry and deals with the study of points, lines and *planes* in space; figures with 3 *dimensions*.

gill. A fluid measure of 4 ounces.

Girard, Albert (jih-rard'), 1595–1632. A Dutch mathematician whose works contained the earliest use of *brackets,* and a geometrical interpretation of the *negative* sign. He gave us the first abbreviations, sin and tan for sine and tangent.

gnomon (no'mon). A vertical column used as a sun dial by the Greeks. It was placed in the middle of 3 concentric circles so that every 2 hours the end of its shadow passed from one circle to another.

Also, in arithmetic, a *term* of a certain kind of *arithmetical progression* of integers. In geometry, the part of a *parallelogram* which remains after a similar parallelogram has been taken away from one of its corners.

GNOMON

Goldbach's conjecture (gold' bock). States that every even number except 2 is the *sum* of two *prime numbers.* Although no one has yet disproved this, no one has ever proved it to be true for all even numbers.

golden section. A *rectangle* of beautiful proportion, which occurs both in nature and in art. The width and the length, added together, are related to the length alone in the same way that the length is related to the width. A golden section rectangle is constructed like this:

1. DRAW SQUARE

2. COMPASS POINT ON 2

3. EXTEND LINE TO MEET 3

4. COMPLETE RECTANGLE

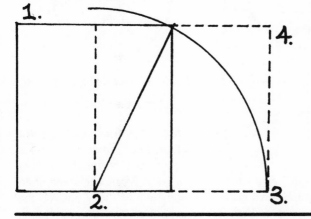

googol (goo'gul). The numeral 1 with a hundred zeros after it. A googolplex is the numeral 1 with a googol of zeros after it.

grain. A unit of weight; $\frac{1}{7000}$ of a pound or 64.8 milligrams. See *table p. 216.*

gram. In the metric system, a unit of weight; 100 centigrams or 1000 milligrams; approximately the weight of one cubic centimeter of water at 4 degrees Centigrade. See *tables pp. 219–220.*

graphs. A bar graph is a set of parallel line segments whose lengths represent quantities for easy comparison.

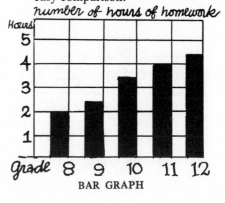

number of hours of homework

BAR GRAPH

A broken-line graph is a set of points connected by line segments. It is usually used to show a trend.

Average of English marks

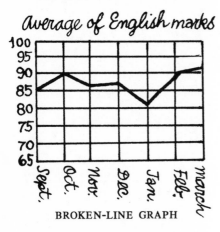

BROKEN-LINE GRAPH

A picture graph, sometimes called a pictograph, uses symbols instead of lines or bars.

Number of books per family borrowed from library.

PICTOGRAPH

EACH SYMBOL (▭) IS 1 BOOK

A circle graph shows the relationship of all the parts to the whole.

How Bill spends a day

CIRCLE GRAPH

René Descartes, the inventor of *analytic geometry,* found a way to picture *linear equations* in graph form. The graph of an equation is the graph of the *solutions* to the equation.

GRAPH OF A LINEAR EQUATION

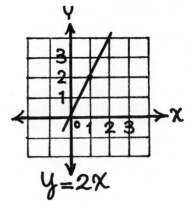

$$y = 2x$$

greater than (or more than). A term referring to an *inequality* between numbers. The symbol is > with the point toward the smaller number. 7 > 6 means 7 is greater than 6. See *less than.*

greatest common factor or greatest common divisor. The largest number that is a *divisor* of a *set* of numbers. For example: the greatest common divisor of 30 and 24 is 6. The greatest common divisor is sometimes written G.C.D. See *Euclidean algorithm.*

greatest possible error. Half of the smallest division on any measuring scale. If a measurement were $1\frac{1}{2}$, the greatest possible error would be $\frac{1}{4}''$, because the indicated measure is $\frac{1}{2}''$. The actual length of a measurement of $1\frac{1}{2}''$ is somewhere between $1\frac{1}{4}''$ and $1\frac{3}{4}''$. (Abbreviated G.P.E.)

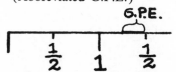

Greeks, mathematics of. The Greeks were the first to love mathematics for itself alone, and not to use it for purely practical reasons. They separated it into *mathematica* (pure mathematics) and *arithmetica* (practical mathematics). Many of the great mathematicians worked at *Alexandria. Euclid* wrote his *Elements* and founded the School of Mathematics there. *Hipparchus,* the inventor of trigonometry worked there; so did *Apollonius,* the discoverer of *conic sections. Archimedes* studied there. The Greeks were great geometers. They tried to square the *circle,* double the *cube,* and *trisect* an angle.

Their numeration system, based on the letters of the Greek alphabet, was awkward. (A little mark next to a letter meant that it was being used as a numeral):

$$a'\ \beta'\ \gamma'\ \delta'\ \epsilon'\ \varsigma'\ \zeta'\ \eta'\ \theta'$$
$$1\ \ 2\ \ 3\ \ 4\ \ 5\ \ 6\ \ 7\ \ 8\ \ 9$$
$$\iota'\ \kappa'\ \lambda'\ \mu'\ \nu'\ \xi'\ o'\ \pi'\ \varphi'$$
$$10\ 20\ 30\ 40\ 50\ 60\ 70\ 80\ 90$$
$$\rho'\ \sigma'\ \tau'\ \upsilon'\ \phi'\ \chi'\ \psi'\ \omega'\ \pi'$$
$$100\ 200\ 300\ 400\ 500\ 600\ 700\ 800\ 900$$

grid. A grating made by crossing lines at right angles, such as the grid used for making a *graph.*

gross. A collection or set of 144 things; 12 dozen.

gross weight. The weight of a container and its contents.

GROSS WEIGHT

group. A mathematics system with a *set* of *elements* and one *binary operation* with the following properties:

1. The set is *closed* under the operation.

2. The operation is *associative*.

3. It has an *identity element*.

4. There must be an *inverse element* for every member of the set.

5. If the group has a *commutative property,* it is known as a *commutative group.*

The *integers* form a group under addition. Zero is the identity element and every element such as −5 has an inverse such as +5. See *field.*

grouping. Arranging things in larger units, as grouping by two's or five's. In the *decimal system* things are grouped into tens (called the *base*). In the *duodecimal system* things are grouped into twelves. In the

PLACE VALUE CHART		
HUNDREDS	TENS	ONES
2	4	3

243 = 2 GROUPS OF 100, 4 GROUPS OF 10 AND 3 GROUPS OF 1

decimal system, *place value* gives us a way of writing about groups of ten. Usually there is a new way of writing the next larger group. Primitive man may have counted sheep individually by pebbles, and then used a larger stone for each group of ten, just as a dime represents our way of grouping ten pennies.

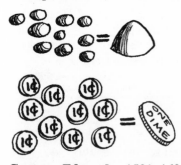

Gunter, Edmund, 1581–1626. An English mathematician who in 1620 built the first *logarithm* scale.

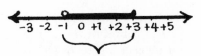

HALF-OPEN INTERVAL

H

h. Abbreviation for *hour* or *height*. h may mean the *line segment* AD or the length of the line segment.

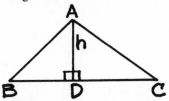

ha. Abbreviation for *hectare*.

half. One of two equal parts into which something is divided.

half-closed interval. The symbol used is [ ). [−1, 3) means all the numbers greater or equal to − 1 and less than 3.

CLOSED END   OPEN END
OF INTERVAL   OF INTERVAL

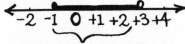

HALF-CLOSED INTERVAL

half-line. Any one *point* on a *line* separates the line into two half-lines. The point is usually not considered part of either half-line.

HALF-LINES

half-open interval. The symbol used is ( ]. (−1, 3] means all numbers greater than −1 and less than or equal to 3.

half-plane. A line divides the *plane* into two half-planes. The line is usually not considered part of either half-plane.

HALF-PLANE

half-space. A *plane* divides *space* into two half-spaces (like cutting a ball into two equal parts).

Hamilton, Sir William, 1805–1865. An Irish mathematician who made many contributions to the fields of optics and mechanics. His "Elements of Quaternions," issued in 1886, is said to have been as great an advance over previous *analytic geometry* as analytic geometry was over *Euclidean geometry*.

harmonic mean. The harmonic mean between two numbers is a number whose *reciprocal* is the *arithmetic mean* of the reciprocals of the numbers. For example, the harmonic mean between 3 and 4 is $\frac{24}{7}$. Usually a table of reciprocals is used, so figuring is not necessary.

RECIPROCAL OF $3 = \frac{1}{3}$

RECIPROCAL OF $4 = \frac{1}{4}$

ARITHMETIC MEAN BETWEEN

$\frac{1}{3}$ *and* $\frac{1}{4} = \frac{7}{24}$

HARMONIC MEAN $\frac{24}{7}$

harmonic progression. A sequence of numbers whose *reciprocals* form an *arithmetic progression*. $\frac{1}{2}$, $\frac{1}{4}$, $\frac{1}{6}$, $\frac{1}{8}$ is a harmonic progression because $\frac{2}{1}$, $\frac{4}{1}$, $\frac{6}{1}$, $\frac{8}{1}$ is an arithmetic progression.

Harriot, Thomas (har'ee-ut), 1560–1621. English mathematician and astronomer. He was tutor to Sir Walter Raleigh who sent him to Virginia, where he made one of the first large-scale statistical surveys. He made important contributions to algebra, introducing new symbols and notations.

heap. A collection of things lying one on another. In ancient Egypt, the symbol for the word heap indicated an unknown quantity. The symbol used by *Diophantus* to represent an unknown may have stood for the Greek word heap.

Hebrew number symbols were letters, like the Greek number symbols:

See *aleph null.*

hecta. Prefix meaning hundred.

hectare (hek'tair). In the metric system, 10,000 square meters or 2.47 acres. See *table p. 220.*

hectogram. In the metric system, 100 grams or about 3.52 ounces in *avoirdupois* weight. See *table p. 219.*

hectoliter. In the metric system, 100 liters. See *table p. 219.*

hectometer. In the metric system, 100 meters, or about 328 feet. See *table p. 219.*

height. See *altitude.*

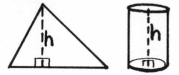

helix (hee'liks). A *spiral;* a curve which lies on a cylinder or cone. It cuts the elements of a figure at a constant angle.

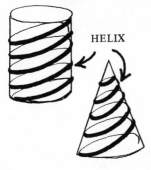

HELIX

hemisphere. Half of a sphere, bounded by a *great circle.*

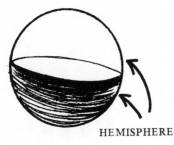

HEMISPHERE

hepta. Prefix meaning seven.

heptagon (hep'tah-gon). A *polygon* having 7 sides.

heptahedron (hep'tah-heed'run). A solid figure with 7 faces.

Hermite, Charles (air-meet'), 1822–1901. A French mathematician who made valuable contributions to the theory of numbers, the theory of elliptic functions and the theory of equations.

Hero of Alexandria (or Heron). A mathematician and inventor who lived some time between the 2nd century B.C. and the 3rd century A.D. He wrote on the measurement of geometric figures and is believed to have found a formula for measuring the area of a triangle. He invented many devices powered by water, steam or compressed air, including a steam engine.

Hero's formula, named after Hero, is a formula for finding the area of a triangle in terms of the lengths of sides a, b, c.

$$A = \sqrt{s\ (s-a)\ (s-b)\ (s-c)}$$

where s = ½ (a + b + c)

hexa. Prefix meaning six.

hexagon (heks'uh-gon). A *polygon* having 6 sides.

hexagram. A geometric figure made by 2 *equilateral* triangles, with a *concentric* center and parallel sides.

HEXAGRAM

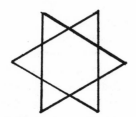

hexahedron. A *polyhedron* with 6 faces.

A CUBE IS A
HEXAHEDRON
TOO

DAVID
HILBERT

Hilbert, David, 1862–1943. A German mathematician who wrote "The Foundations of Geometry," which established geometry as an abstract study of purely formal character, depending upon a set of *postulates.*

Hindu-Arabic numeration system. The system of symbols and *place value* which the Hindus used to express numbers. Our modern system of numerals is derived from it.

0 ? 2 ⶾ 8 ⴄ Ɛ U Z 8
0 1 2 3 4 5 6 7 8 9

Hindus, mathematics of. The Hindus, about 1500 years ago, made the greatest contribution ever to a system for expressing numbers. They used the idea of *place value* and of base ten. The mathematicians of India also wrote and worked with fractions the way we do today. Their mathematics was passed on to us through the Arabs, so we call it the Hindu-Arabic system.

Hipparchus (hih-park′us). Second-century B.C. Greek astronomer and mathematician. He discussed the procession of the equinoxes, made the first chart of the heavens and suggested a method of determining longitude. He developed the first system of trigonometry.

Hippocrates (of Chios) (hip-pock′rah-teez), 440 (?) B.C. One of the greatest Greek geometricians. He wrote the first elementary textbook on geometry, which was probably the basis for the geometry of Euclid. He is supposed to have been the first to use letters to name points and lines in geometric drawings. He proved many propositions, among them that similar *elements* of a circle contain equal angles. His best known discoveries were concerned with the *quadrature* of the circle and the duplication of the cube.

histogram. In statistics, a graph showing a *frequency distribution*. It is usually drawn on

HISTOGRAM

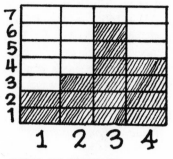

CASES OF MEASLES
DURING 4 WEEKS OF MAY

paper laid out in small rectangles:
This is sometimes called a column diagram.

horizontal line. One parallel to, or on a level with, the horizon.

horizontal change. The difference of the x-*coordinates*. This difference may be expressed as $|x_2 - x_1|$ or Δx.

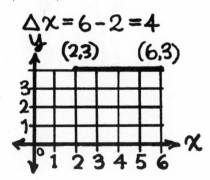

hour. A measure of time, equal
to $\frac{1}{24}$ of a day, or 60 minutes.
Huygens, Christian (hai'genz),
1629–1695. A Dutch mathe-
matician and physicist. He im-
proved telescopic lenses,
invented the clock pendulum
and developed a wave theory
of light.
hyperbola (hy-puhr'buh-lah). See
conic sections.

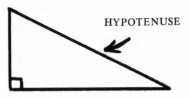

right triangle opposite the
right angle.
hypothesis (hy-poth'uh-sis). A
proposition assumed or given
as true in order to prove something else.

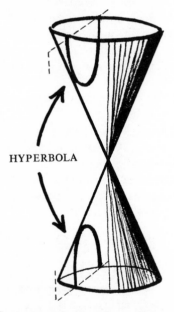

HYPERBOLA

I

I. The Roman numeral for 1.
i. Designates an *imaginary number* with the property $i^2 = -1$.
icosahedron (eye-coh'sa-heed'
run). A *polyhedron* having 20
faces.

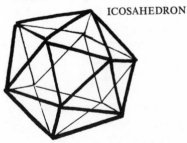

ICOSAHEDRON

hypercomplex numbers. See *quaternions*.

hypotenuse (hy-pot'uh-noos). The
longest side of a plane right
triangle; the side of a plane

identical. The property of being
exactly alike. For geometric
figures, see *congruent*.

identical sets. See *equal sets.*

identities. Statements of *equality* that are true for all meaningful values of the *variables.* For example, $2y + 4y = 6y$. For any value of y, the statement is true.

identity element. The sum of 0 and any number is that number. $4 + 0 = 4$. The number 0 is called the *additive identity.* The product of 1 and any number is that number. $1 \times 7 = 7$. The number 1 is called the *multiplicative identity.*

if . . . then. See *conditional open sentence.*

imaginary number, pure. A *complex number* is of the form $a + bi$ where a and b are *real numbers* and $i^2 = -1$. When $a = 0$ and $b \neq 0$, we have a pure imaginary number.

implication. See *conditional open sentence, hypothesis.*

improper fraction. See *fraction.* The expression "improper fraction," which is not used as often as formerly, means a fraction whose numerator is larger than or equal to the denominator.

$$\frac{3}{3}, \frac{8}{3}$$

inch. A unit of length; approximately 2.54 centimeters, $\frac{1}{12}$ of a foot. See *tables pp. 216, 217, 220.*

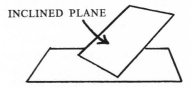
INCLINED PLANE

inclined plane. A *plane oblique* to another horizontal plane.

inclusion symbols. See *braces, brackets, parentheses, table pp. 210–211.*

$$\{ \quad \} \quad [\quad] \quad (\quad)$$
INCLUSION SYMBOLS

incommensurable line segments. *Line segments* with no common measure.

inconsistent equations. Two *equations* that have no common solution set. $y = x + 1$; $y = x + 3$. Their graphs are parallel lines with no point in common.

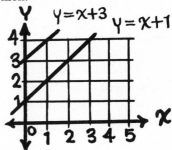

increment (in'kreh-ment). An amount added to or subtracted from a value of a *variable*. If x is a variable, Δx usually represents a small increment.

incurvate. Curving, usually inward.

independent equations. Two *consistent equations* having only one solution in common.

$$x-y=3$$
$$x+y=7$$

CONSISTENT EQUATIONS

independent event. If you toss a coin and it comes up heads, there is still a 50–50 chance that it will come up heads on the next toss. Each toss is an independent event.

independent variable. In an *ordered pair*, (x, y), x may be the independent variable. The values assigned to y depend on the values given to x. So y is the *dependent variable*. See *function*.

indeterminate equation. An *equation* containing more than one *variable*, such as $5x + 6y = 9$.

index (pl. indices). In $\sqrt[3]{8}$ the index is 3. If no index is indicated, as in $\sqrt{4}$, the index is 2.

index number. In *statistics*, a number used to compare some quantity, such as cost of living at different times. If the cost of living index is set at 100 based on 1957–1959 prices, and if it reaches 120 in 1966, one can see how much it has gone up.

India, mathematics of. See *Hindu-Arabic numeration system*.

indirect measurement. It may be impossible to measure a particular distance directly with a measuring instrument. However, if other measurements can be made and a formula used, the particular distance is said to be found indirectly.

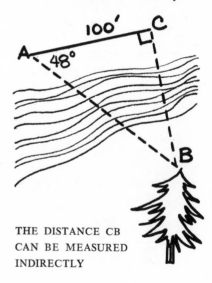

THE DISTANCE CB CAN BE MEASURED INDIRECTLY

induction, mathematical. A method for proving a proposition. A proposition holds true for the first case when tested. Assume the proposition is true for the *n*th case. Check the proposition for the next case after *n*. If this case is true, then we say the proposition is true for all cases.

inequality. A sentence stating that one quantity is greater than (>), less than (<), or not equal to (≠) another quantity.

INEQUALITIES

infinite. Not *finite* or countable, endless.

infinite sequence. A *set* of *elements* in *one-to-one correspondence* with the *natural numbers*. For example, 2, 4, 6, 8, 10 . . . There is no last term in the *sequence*.

infinite series. Any indicated sum of an *infinite set* of terms. For example $1 + 2 + 3 + 4 + 5 \ldots + n + \ldots$

infinite set. A set whose elements cannot be counted because they are unlimited. For example, the set of even numbers is infinite: $\{2, 4, 6, 8, 10 \ldots\}$. There is no last even number.

INITIAL POINT

initial point. See *terminal point*.

inscribed angle. An angle whose *vertex* is on the circle and whose sides intersect the circle.

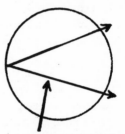

INSCRIBED ANGLE

inscribed circle. A circle inscribed in a *polygon*. Each side of the polygon has only one point in common with the circle.

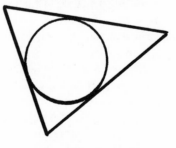

INSCRIBED CIRCLE

inscribed polygon. One whose vertices are on a circle.

installment buying. Buying goods for a part of the total price, then paying the balance in equal payments at regular intervals, usually with interest added to the original price.

integer (in'teh-jer). −3 is an integer. So are −2, −1, 0, +1, +2, +3 . . . Those integers greater than zero are called positive integers. Integers less than zero are negative integers.

integral calculus. The branch of mathematics which is concerned with finding the *limit* of a *sum* of *terms,* and may be used for determining the *area* bounded by a curve or the work done by a force. See *calculus.*

integral domain. A mathematical system. A *set* of *elements* for which two *operations,* addition and multiplication, are defined, so that:

1. $a + b$ and $a \times b$ determine *unique elements* from the set of elements.
2. The *distributive,* two *commutative* and two *associative properties* are true.
3. The *additive identity* and *multiplicative identity* exist.
4. For each element a, there is an element −a, such that $a + (-a) = 0$.
5. If $c \neq 0$ and $ca = cb$, then $a = b$. The set of *integers* is an example of an integral domain.

integral exponents. $4^2 = 16$, $4^0 = 1$, $4^{-2} = \dfrac{1}{16}$.

See *exponent, integer.*

intercept. To cut, as a line intercepting a circle.

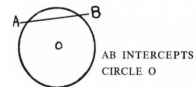

AB INTERCEPTS
CIRCLE O

The line $y = x + 3$ intercepts the y-axis at $(0, 3)$.
3 is called the y-intercept.

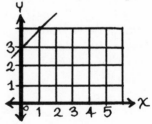

interest. A payment for the use of money borrowed.

interest, compound. See *compound interest.*

interior. The interior of ∠ ABC is the *intersection* of two *half-planes.* It does not include the angle.

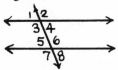

INTERIOR

interior angles. On a *polygon,* the angles in the interior of the polygon. When parallel lines are intersected by a *transversal,* the angles 3, 4, 5, 6 are interior angles.

interpolation. A method of finding values between any two known values.

intersection. A *set* of *elements* two given sets have in common is called the intersection of the two sets. The symbol for intersection is ∩, sometimes called *cap.* For example, if set A = {0, 1, 2, 3, 4} and set B = {0, 2, 4, 6} then the intersection of sets A and B is A ∩ B = {0, 2, 4}.

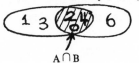

A ∩ B

intersection of lines. Two lines may have one point in common. Point A is the intersection of l_1 and l_2. Two *parallel* lines have no point in common. Their intersection is said to be empty.

intersection of planes. The intersection of two *planes* is a line. See *dihedral angle.*

INTERSECTION
OF PLANES

intersection of regions of circles. The common *regions* of two or more circles.

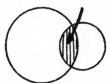

interval. A *set* containing all the numbers between two given numbers, and the two given numbers, or one of them, or neither one. If it is a *closed interval* it contains the two given numbers and all numbers between them. See *half-closed* or *half-open interval.*

invariant. Description of a property that is not altered by certain change. *Klein* classified geometries according to the invariant properties of their figures. The 4 invariant properties of *Euclidean geometry* are *translation, rotation, reflection* and *dilation.* In *topology,* figures are preserved although they are constantly deformed. See *affine geometry, point-set theory.*

inverse. Opposite. See *additive inverse, multiplicative inverse.*

inverse variation. Some *ordered pairs* are shown in the table. The product of the members of each pair is *constant.* (In this table it is 2.) Such a *function* is called an inverse variation. We say y varies inversely as x varies, and write $y = \frac{k}{x}$, where x and y are *variables* and k is a constant.

$$Y = \frac{2}{x} \text{ OR } XY = 2$$

involution. The raising of a quantity to a given *power.*

irrational numbers. *Rational numbers* can be expressed in the form $\frac{a}{b}$ where a and b are *integers* and $b \neq 0$. Irrational numbers are *real numbers* that are not rational. For example, $\sqrt{2}$ is irrational.

isogonal (eye-sog'uh-nal). Having equal angles.

isosceles triangle (eye-sos'uh-leez). A triangle in which two sides have the same measure.

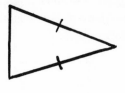

J

Jacobi, Carl, 1804–1851. A German mathematician who, like *Abel,* presented a new branch of mathematics called the theory of elliptic functions. His statement "One must always invert" (an operation or procedure) has led to many inventions and scientific discoveries.

join. To unite or add. It is also used to show the *set* made by the *union* of two sets. The "join" of sets A and B (A∪B)

$$\text{IF SET A} = \{1, 2, 3, 4, 5\}$$
$$\text{AND SET B} = \{4, 5, 6, 7, \}$$
$$\text{A} \cup \text{B} = \{1, 2, 3, 4, 5, 6, 7\}$$

consists of the members that belong either to A or to B or to both.

Join, in geometry, is to connect *points* by straight *line segments.*

Jones, William, 1675–1749. English writer. The first person to use π to represent the ratio of circumference to the diameter of a circle. He did this in 1706. However, it was only after *Euler* used it in 1737 that the symbol π came into more general use. π is approximately equal to 3.14 or $\frac{22}{7}$. See *Ludolphian number.*

Jordan's theorem. In *topology,* one of the theorems presented by the French mathematician Camille Jordan (1838–1922). It states: Every *closed curve* in the plane that does not cross itself divides the plane into an inside and an outside. Strange as it seems, Jordan's proof of the theorem was invalid and it was Veblen who finally offered a valid proof.

joule (jool). A work unit of 10 million *ergs,* named for James Joule, an English mathematician and physicist who was the first to study the relationship between work and heat.

K

k. Symbol for a *constant.* In general, a *function* described by $y = kx$ is a *direct variation.* k is called the constant of variation.

Kasner, Edward, 1878–1955. An American mathematician best known for his work in higher geometry. He coined the terms (suggested by his 9-year-old nephew) *googol* and googolplex.

Kelvin, Lord (William Thomson), 1824–1907. British mathematician and physicist, invented the absolute temperature scale, sometimes called the *Kelvin scale.* In 1872 he built the *Kelvin machine,* which was a major contribution to modern calculators.

Kelvin machine. A machine built by Lord *Kelvin,* made of pulleys, weights and connecting cords, for use in predicting tides. The machine gave a physical measurement that was in proportion to the tide at a given time. It was one of the forerunners of modern *computers.*

Kelvin scale. A very precise standard of temperature measurement, based upon a constant-volume gas pressure thermometer. Zero on the Kelvin scale is −273° C.

The Kelvin scale is used to measure color which, as a form of light, is a form of heat, too. A degree Kelvin is a measure of the temperature—and so of the differences—in color. The temperature of noontime summer sunlight is about 6000 degrees Kelvin.

JOHANNES
KEPLER

Kepler, Johannes, 1571–1630. A German mathematician and one of the founders of modern astronomy. His three laws of

planetary motion state:

1. That the orbit of each planet is an *ellipse,* with the center of the sun as one of the *foci.*

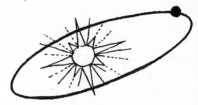

2. That the imaginary line joining the center of each planet with the center of the sun moves over equal areas of the ellipse in equal periods of time.

3. That the time each planet takes to complete its journey around the sun is proportional to the *cube* of its *mean* distance from the sun.

Kepler, with *Desargues* and *Galileo,* was a connecting link between the mathematics of the Renaissance and the mathematics of modern times. He prepared the way for *Cavalieri, Leibniz* and *Newton.*

kev. A unit of energy, equivalent to 1000 electron volts.

kilo. A prefix meaning 1000.

kilocycle. A unit of the frequency of electromagnetic waves, equal to 1000 cycles.

kilogram. The metric unit of mass. It is the mass of a special platinum-iridium cylinder. It is approximately 2.2 pounds. See *tables pp. 219–220.*

kiloliter. In the metric system, a unit of *volume,* equal to 1000 liters. See *table p. 219.*

kilometer. In the metric system, 1000 meters, a measure of distance, equal to approximately .62 mile or 3280 feet, 10 inches. See *table p. 219.*

kilowatt. A measure of electrical power, 1000 watts.

Klein, Felix, 1849–1925. A German mathematician who made many contributions to *topology.* He is noted for his work in the theory of *functions* and in *geometry.* He codified diverse forms of geometry. He claimed that geometries were investigations of properties of geometric figures that do not change under certain transformations such as *rotation.*

Klein bottle. A *manifold* in *topology* which looks like a bottle but has no insides or outsides, and is a one-sided surface.

knot. A speed of 1 *nautical mile,* approximately 6,080.2 feet per hour. If a ship travels at the rate of 24 knots (never 24 knots per hour), it is moving at the rate of 24 nautical miles per hour. See *table p. 218.*

Königsberg Bridge problem (kern′ igs-burg). A problem, used by Leonhard *Euler,* which was one of the beginning steps in *topology.* The City of Königsberg has seven bridges, as illustrated, and the problem was to see whether a person could start anywhere and cross each bridge without crossing any one of them twice. (Euler proved that it was impossible.) The bridges were arranged like this:

THE KLEIN
BOTTLE WAS
INVENTED BY
FELIX KLEIN

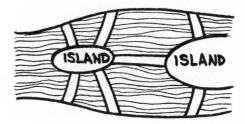

Kowalewski, Sonya (koh-va-lev′ skee), 1850–1891. A Russian mathematician, one of the most famous women mathematicians of all time. She was a friend and pupil of *Weierstrass.* Her work with *infinite series* made possible the discoveries of *Einstein* and other atomic physicists.

L

L. The Roman numeral for fifty.
l. Symbol for *liter.*

A line may be named line l.

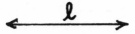

l is also used as a *variable* in such formulas as A = lw.

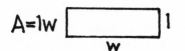

label. Triangle ABC is labeled: △ABC.

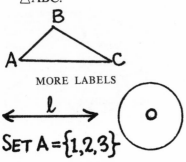

MORE LABELS

Lagrange, Joseph Louis, 1736–1813. A French mathematician, sometimes called the most outstanding of the 18th century. He was the head of the Committee on Weights and Measures which adopted the *metric system,* used by many countries today. He did a great deal to make the calculus rigorous, solved some of the problems of *Fermat,* wrote papers that led to many of the later contributions of *Laplace* and other mathematicians and played an important part in verifying the theory of gravitation stated by *Newton.* Besides his work in pure mathematics, he also wrote on mechanics and astronomy.

PIERRE SIMON LAPLACE

Laplace, Pierre Simon de (lah-plahs′), 1749–1827. A French mathematician who, with *Bernoulli,* was one of the origi-

117

nators of the field of *probability*. With *Legendre* and *Gauss* he evolved the theory of least squares. Some of his work opened important developments in hydrodynamics, electricity and the study of gravitation. Perhaps his most important book dealt with celestial mechanics and gave an analytical discussion of the solar system, including methods for calculating the motions of the planets and the tides.

larger than. See *greater than.*

lateral. Side.

lateral area. In a *prism,* the sum of the areas of the *faces* or surfaces.

lateral surface. The curved surface of a figure such as a *cylinder* or a *cone.* The lateral faces of a *pyramid, prism,* etc.

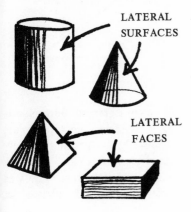

LATERAL
SURFACES

LATERAL
FACES

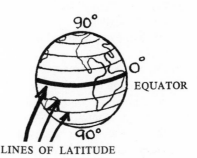

LINES OF LATITUDE

latitude. The number of degrees in an arc of a *meridian* north or south from the equator. Lines (or parallels) of latitude run parallel to the equator, and with lines of *longitude* locate precisely any point on the earth's surface. They are numbered in degrees of latitude. 0° is the equator, and 90° north or south is at the poles.

lattice. On this drawing the points

(0, 1) (0, 2) (0, 3) (1, 1)
(1, 2) (2, 1) (2, 2) (2, 3)

are graphed. The lines through the points form a lattice. The points where they intersect are called lattice points.

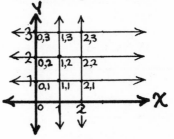

laws. See *operations, properties, arithmetic laws.*

LCD. See *least common denominator.*

LCM. See *least common multiple.*

least common denominator. (Also called *least common multiple.*) The least common multiple of the *denominators* of two or more fractions. The least common denominator of $\frac{5}{6}, \frac{3}{4}, \frac{1}{2}$, is 12, because 12 is the lowest number into which 6, 4 and 2 can be divided.

least common multiple. The least common multiple of a set of *counting numbers* is the smallest counting number which is divisible by each of the numbers in the set. Some *multiples* of 6 are: 6, 12, 18, 24, 30, . . . Some multiples of 4 are: 4, 8, 12, 16, 20, 24, . . . Notice that 12 and 24 are common multiples of 6 and 4. The least common multiple of 6 and 4 is 12.

ledger. In bookkeeping, an *account* book.

left. Opposite of *right.* It is usually used in discussing *nega-*

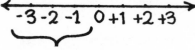

POINTS TO THE
LEFT OF 0 POINT

tive numbers, or those numbers associated with points to the left of the zero point on the *number line.*

Legendre, Adrien-Marie (luh-jahn'druh), 1752–1833. A French mathematician whose simplification of the geometry of *Euclid* is still in use today. He made many contributions to the fields of calculus, geometry and physics. *Laplace,* because he was jealous, used his influence to keep Legendre from gaining public recognition.

legs of a triangle. The sides of a right triangle *perpendicular* to each other. They have a common *vertex,* and are *adjacent* to the right angle.

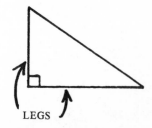

LEGS

Leibniz (or Leibnitz), Baron Gottfried Wilhelm von (lyep'nits), 1646–1716. A famous German mathematician, philosopher and statesman, who was interested in all phases of

GOTTFRIED
WILHELM
VON LEIBNIZ

knowledge. He invented the calculus, the chief advance in mathematics during the first half of the 18th century. There is still argument over whether Leibniz knew about the work of *Newton* on the calculus, or discovered it independently. Through the years the best of the two theories has been combined and the Leibniz system of notation is now used.

length of a line segment. The measure of a *line segment*. If the line segment has numbers associated with its *endpoints,* the length of the line segment is the *positive* difference of the numbers associated with its endpoints. The length of line segment $\overline{AB}$ is $5 - 1$, or 4.

Leonardo of Pisa, 1175–1230, (also known as Fibonacci). An Italian mathematician who was one of the first to introduce the *Arabic numeration system* into Europe. One of his works, the "Liber Abaci," shows how to solve various kinds of *equations* and uses letters as geometric symbols. For over 200 years it was a leading authority on mathematics. Perhaps his best-known contribution is the *sequence* known as *Fibonacci numbers.*

less than (or smaller than). A term referring to an *inequality* between two numbers. The symbol is $<$, with the point toward the smaller number. $6 < 7$ means 6 is less than 7. See *greater than.*

light-year. The distance light travels in one year, 6000 billion miles. Most of the stars are more than 100 light-years from earth.

like terms. If *terms* are the same with respect to the *variable(s)* and *exponent(s)* of these variables, we say they are like terms. For example, 3x and $-12x$ are like terms; $3ab^2$ and $-7ab^2$ are like terms.

Lilāvati. See *Bhaskara.*

limit. A concept that deals with the idea of "almost equal to." If we continue to add the fractions below to others in this series, the sum will never reach 2. The limit of the sum is 2.

$1 + \frac{1}{2} + \frac{1}{4} + \frac{1}{8} + \frac{1}{16} + \frac{1}{32} + \ldots$ is 2.

line. A particular set of *points*. Lines in geometry extend in two directions without end.

In mathematics, unless otherwise stated, lines are always thought to be straight. When drawing a representation of a line, arrows are put at the ends to show that lines extend infinitely.

See *line segment, ray, concurrent lines, parallel lines.*

linear equation. The *graph* of a first-*degree equation* is a straight line. Such an equation is called a linear equation.

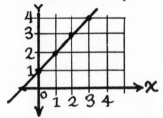

GRAPH OF A LINEAR EQUATION $Y = X + 1$

linear measurement. A measure of length of line segments or one-dimensional figures.

linear perspective. A picture or drawing which gives the illusion of depth.

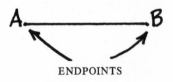

LINEAR PERSPECTIVE

line graph. See *graph.*

line of sight. An imaginary "line" from the observer to an object.

line segment. The union of two *points* on a *line* and all the points between them. The two points are called the *endpoints* of the line segment. See *ray.*

A————————B

ENDPOINTS

link. See *table p. 217.*

liquid measure. See *table p. 218.*

liter. A unit of *volume* in the metric system; the volume of 1 kilogram of water at 4° centigrade. See *table pp. 219–220.*

literal equations. The *formula* which uses letters is the most important kind of literal equation. For example, $I = prt$, $S = \frac{1}{2} gt^2$ are literal equations. See *table of formulas pp. 212–215.*

literal numbers. An expression sometimes used to mean a letter denoting any one of a *set* of numbers. For example, n may be used to represent any *whole number.*

list price. The price at which an object is listed in a catalogue or other publication.

loan. A sum of money that is borrowed and must be repaid, usually with interest.

NIKOLAI
LOBACHEVSKI

Lobachevski, Nikolai (loh-ba-chev'skee), 1793–1856. A Russian mathematician, contemporary of *Bolyai,* who also challenged the *parallel postulate* of *Euclid.* He assumed that through a *point* outside a given *line* there are at least two lines *parallel* to the given line. He then constructed a geometry which is now one of the *non-Euclidean geometries.* In this geometry, the sum of the angles of a triangle is not greater than 180°, and the smaller the triangle is in area, the closer to 180° is the sum of the angles.

locus (loh'kus). Any set of points that satisfies certain conditions and no points that do not. For example, the locus of points in a plane a given distance from a fixed point in the plane is a circle whose center is the given point.

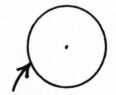

LOCUS OF POINTS A GIVEN
DISTANCE FROM A FIXED POINT

locus of an equation. A set of points and only those points whose *coordinates* are solutions of an *equation*. For example, the locus of y = x + 3 is a line.

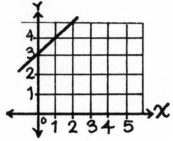

logarithm (log'a-rith'm). In 10^3 = 1000, we call 1000 the number, 10 the *base* and 3 the *exponent*. The logarithm of the number 1000 is the exponent 3 to which the base 10 must be raised to give the number 1000. Since $10^3 = 1000$, the logarithm of 1000 to the base 10 is the exponent 3.

A logarithm (log) of a number is the exponent to which a base must be raised to produce the number. Log 9 (to the base 3) is 2 because $9 = 3^2$.

Logarithms simplify many long mathematical operations. Where you would have to multiply numbers, the answer can be found by adding logarithms.

Tables of logarithms are used to help us find the logarithms of numbers. For example, the log of 427 to base 10 is approximately 2.6304. Thus 427 = $10^{2.6304}$. See *Napier, table of logarithms pp. 222–223.*

THIS PART OF THE LOGARITHM IS CALLED THE MANTISSA

THIS PART OF THE LOGARITHM IS CALLED THE CHARACTERISTIC

logic, mathematical. *Deductive reasoning* or logic as associated with pure mathematics. *Leibniz* in 1666 used symbols to develop mathematical reasoning. It was further developed by *Boole* and others, and is now considered the basis of all new mathematics because its laws can be applied to all mathematics.

longitude. The distance east or west of a prime *meridian,* usually that through Greenwich, England. Longitude is computed in degrees, east or west from 0° to 180°. Imaginary lines called meridians, running from pole to pole, connect all

MERIDIANS ARE
LINES OF LONGITUDE

places of the same longitude.
Meridians cross the equator
and the other parallels of *latitude* at right angles. Roughly
every 15° of longitude means
a one hour's difference in time.

long ton, 2240 pounds, or 20 long
hundredweight, a common
measure of weight in international shipping. A long ton,
which is equal in weight to 35
cubic feet of sea water, measures a displacement ton. Displacement is the amount of
water any ship displaces. See
table p. 216.

lowest common denominator
(LCD). See *least common denominator.*

lowest terms. A *fractional numeral* whose *numerator* and
denominator have 1 as the
only common factor. ¾ is in
lowest terms or, as it is sometimes called, in simplest form.

Ludolphian number (lu-dolf'ee-
un). Another term for π (*pi*),
which in 1615 was calculated
to 35 digits by Ludolph van
Ceulen, a German (or Dutch)
mathematician, who worked on
the problem most of his life.
On his tombstone, π is the only
epitaph.

lumen (lu'men). A measure of
the amount of light falling on
a surface one foot away from
a light of one candle power.

lux. The unit of illumination or
light equal to the amount received at a distance` of one
meter from a standard light
source. It is equal to one lumen
per square meter.

M

M. The Roman numeral for
1000.

m. Symbol for meter, mile.

Mach number (mock). The speed
of an object compared to the
speed of sound in air, approximately 1100 feet per second.
Mach 1 is the speed of sound;
Mach 2 is twice the speed of
sound.

Maclaurin, Colin, 1698–1746. A
Scottish mathematician who, in

1740, shared the prize awarded by the French Academy of Sciences with Daniel *Bernouilli* and *Euler.* He made contributions to geometry, astronomy and other branches of mathematics, but is remembered chiefly for coming to the defense of *Newton* and the calculus, and giving geometric proofs for Newton's conclusions.

magic squares. Numbers arranged in a square so that each *row, column* and *diagonal* adds up to the same total. The earliest known magic square is Chinese and dates back about 3000 years. One of the most famous magic squares was made by the artist Albrecht Dürer in A.D. 1514, and was part of a larger engraving. The square looks like this:

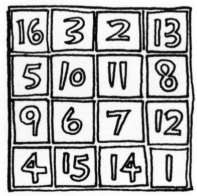

magnitude. Size. It refers to length and volume.

major. Principal or main, as the *major axis* of an ellipse, or the *major arc of a circle.*

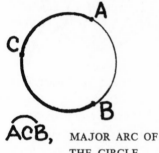

$\overset{\frown}{ACB,}$ MAJOR ARC OF THE CIRCLE

major arc of a circle. An arc larger than a semicircle.

major axis. The longer *axis* in an *ellipse.*

MAJOR AXIS OF AN ELLIPSE

manifold (man'ih-fold). Another term for space. A collection or set of objects.

mantissa (man-tis'sa). See *logarithms.*

2.5391

MANTISSA OF A LOGARITHM

map-coloring problem. See *four-color map problem.*

mapping. If to each *element* of a *set* there is a corresponding *unique* element from another set, then we say there is a mapping of set x in set y. See *correspondence.*

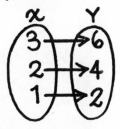

mapping, many-to-one. A *mapping* in which more than one *member* of one *set* is matched with one member of another set.

FAVORITE COLOR

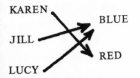

mass. A measure of a body's tendency to resist a change in *velocity.* If you push a brick, then push an empty shoebox, you will see which has the greater mass. Mass is often roughly associated with weight.

MATCHING

$$\text{SET A} = \{1, 2, 3\}$$
$$\Updownarrow \quad \Updownarrow \quad \Updownarrow$$
$$\text{SET B} = \{✏ \; 📎 \; |\}$$

matching. To pair or *associate,* usually in *one-to-one-correspondence.* See *mapping.*
Set A = {a, b, c}
Set B = {comb, chair, table}

mathematica (math'uh-mat'i-kuh). The Greek word for pure mathematics, as opposed to practical arithmetic.

mathematical sentence. A sentence that uses numerals, symbols and sometimes words. It can be either true or false. See *compound* and *conditional open sentence, connective.*

TRUE SENTENCE

$$7 > 3$$

FALSE SENTENCE

$$4 + 2 \neq 6 \times 1$$

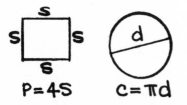

$$P = 4S \qquad C = \pi d$$

mathematical shorthand. A way of writing sentences in mathematics or logic by using *symbols*. For example, we usually think of a formula as mathematical shorthand for some relationship. See *table of symbols pp. 210–212*.

mathematics. The study of relation between objects or quantities, organized so that certain facts can be proved or derived from others by using *logic*. See *applied mathematics, pure mathematics*.

matrices. See *matrix*.

matrix (pl. matrices) (may'triks). A rectangular *array* of *elements*. Mathematical operations are performed on matrices. A matrix might have four numbers or a hundred. Four numbers would be a 2 by 2 matrix.

$$\begin{bmatrix} 1 & 5 \\ 3 & 2 \end{bmatrix} \qquad \begin{bmatrix} 1 & 5 & 6 \\ 3 & 2 & 4 \end{bmatrix}$$

TWO BY TWO MATRIX

THREE BY TWO MATRIX

A hundred might be 10 by 10, or 4 by 25, or any other regular arrangement. Matrices are a way in which complicated mathematical statements can be expressed simply.

Computers are often used in work with matrices. Problems in statistics and economics can be expressed in terms of matrices.

JAMES CLERK MAXWELL

Maxwell, James Clerk, 1831–1879. A great Scottish mathematician and physicist. He won early recognition with mathematical papers and developed the theory of the electromagnetic field on a mathematical basis. He made enormous contributions to physics not only in electromagnetic fields but in the understanding of light, heat, color, gases and dynamics. The unit of magnetic flux, or change, is called a maxwell.

Mayan numeration system (my′-yen). The system of the Mayan Indians of Central America. Any number could be written with only 3 kinds of symbols:

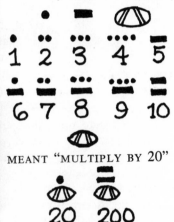

MEANT "MULTIPLY BY 20"

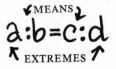

The Mayans had a *place value* system that worked very well.

mean, in statistics. See *central tendency, measures of*

means, in proportion. In $\frac{a}{b} = \frac{c}{d}$, which also can be written a:b = c:d, the terms b and c are called the means. They are the second and third terms of the proportion. When the means of a proportion are the

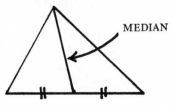

same, as in $\frac{1}{4} = \frac{4}{16}$, either mean is said to be the mean proportional between the first and fourth terms. See *arithmetic mean, geometric mean, harmonic mean.*

measure. To compare to some unit, usually a *standard unit.*

measured length. The measure of an object obtained by using a measuring instrument. Because no instrument is absolutely correct, the measured length is never the same as the *true length.*

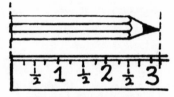

MEASURED LENGTH

median. In *statistics.* See *central tendency, measures of.*

median of a triangle. A *line segment* whose *endpoints* are one *vertex* of a triangle and the midpoint of the side opposite the vertex.

MEDIAN

meet. The word used by *Boole* for *intersection*. In Boolean algebra, A ∩ B is read, "the meet of A and B." See *cap.*

mega. Prefix meaning one million, as in megacycle.

members of an equation. The *algebraic expressions* on either side of the equality sign. x + y = 8 + 3.

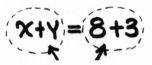

MEMBERS OF AN EQUATION

members of a set. The *elements* of a *set*.

SET A = {6,7,8,9}

MEMBERS OF
THE SET

Menaechmus (mee-nayk′mus), 375–325 B.C. A Greek mathematician. Pupil of *Eudoxus,* he was the first to discuss *conic sections,* which were called Menaechmian triads. The story is told that Menaechmus said to Alexander the Great, "There is no royal road in geometry." The same story is told of Euclid and Ptolemy.

GREGOR
MENDEL

Mendel, Gregor (men′del), 1822–1884. An Austrian priest who showed, by experiments in cross-breeding peas, that certain characteristics are inherited according to the mathematical laws of *probability*.

Menelaus (men-uh-lay′us), c A.D. 100. A Greek astronomer and mathematician who lived in Rome, and who wrote the oldest known work on spherical trigonometry.

mensuration (men-shuh-ray′shun). The process of finding the measure of geometric figures; for example, the length of line segments, the areas of surfaces and the volumes of solids.

Méré, Antoine, Gombauld Chevalier de. See *DeMéré.*

meridian. A *great circle* on the surface of the earth running from pole to pole and cutting the equator at right angles

PRIME MERIDIAN

The prime meridian at Greenwich, England, is 0°. The international *date line* runs roughly along the 180th meridian.

meter. The basic unit of *linear measure* of the metric system, approximately 39.37 inches. See *tables pp. 219–220.*

metric system. A *decimal* system of weights and measures. The standard unit for length is the *meter,* for *mass* the *gram* and for *capacity* the *liter.*

The metric system was adopted first in France. It is now used for practically all scientific measurements. See *Lagrange, tables pp. 219–220.*

metric ton. 1000 kilograms.

micro. Prefix meaning 1/1,000,-000.

midpoint. In a *line segment,* the point that *bisects* the line segment.

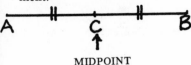

MIDPOINT

mile. A measure of distance, equal to 1760 yards, 5280 feet, or approximately 1.6094 kilometers. See *tables pp. 216, 217.*

mille. The Roman word for thousand, and probably the origin of *mile* (which was a thousand paces of a Roman soldier).

milli. Prefix meaning one thousand, or one-thousandth part.

milliard (mil'yard). The name given to the numeral 1,000,-000,000 in France, Germany and England; in the U.S. it is called 1 *billion.*

milligram. One-thousandth of a *gram.*

million. One thousand times one thousand, or 1,000,000.

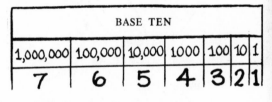

BASE TEN						
1,000,000	100,000	10,000	1000	100	10	1
7	6	5	4	3	2	1

minim. $\frac{1}{60}$ of a fluid dram; the smallest *liquid measure.* See *table p. 218.*

minuend. The name given to the quantity from which another quantity is to be subtracted. In some of the newer texts, the language of *minuend, subtra-*

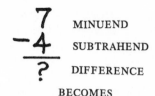

MINUEND

SUBTRAHEND

DIFFERENCE

BECOMES

MISSING ADDEND SUM
ADDEND

hend and *difference* is replaced by *sum, addend,* and *missing addend.*

minor arc of a circle. An *arc* of a circle less than a semicircle.

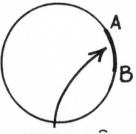

MINOR ARC $\overset{\frown}{AB}$

minus. The name for the symbol — . 8 minus 2 is written 8 — 2 and means that 2 is to be subtracted from 8.

minute. A measure of time, $\frac{1}{60}$ of an hour. A circular measure, $\frac{1}{60}$ of a degree. See *table p. 251.*

mixed algebraic expressions. The sum of a *polynomial* and a *rational expression.*

$$a + \left(\frac{1}{a}\right), \quad 1 + \left(\frac{1}{x}\right)$$

are mixed expressions.

mixed number. A term commonly used to refer to a *mixed numeral.*

mixed numeral. A numeral such as $1\frac{1}{2}$, $7\frac{7}{8}$, $5\frac{3}{4}$. See *fraction.*

Möbius or Moebius, August Ferdinand (mer'bee-us), 1790–1868. A German astronomer and mathematician; a pupil of *Gauss.* His name is given to a one-sided surface known as the *Möbius strip,* which is studied in *topology.* His works, together with those of *Riemann, Lobachevski, Bolyai* and others, appeared at about the same time, and created a revolution in geometry.

Möbius strip. A surface (invented by Möbius) with only one "side." It is made by giving a strip of paper a half-twist and then fastening the ends together. If a line is drawn down

TWIST THE STRIP IN ONE PLACE

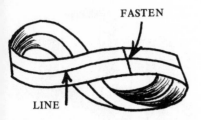

FASTEN

LINE

the middle of the strip, it will
come back to the starting point
after having covered both
"sides" of the paper, without
the pencil being lifted.

mode. In *statistics*. See *central
tendency, measures of*.

modular arithmetic. Sometimes
called clock arithmetic or
finite arithmetic. A *finite set* of
elements is selected, such as 0,
1, 2, 3. *Operations* are defined
on these elements, usually in
table form. It can be shown
that the usual *associative* and
commutative properties hold,
as do other properties. Thus a
small mathematical system is
developed.

+	0	1	2	3
0	0	1	2	3
1	1	2	3	0
2	2	3	0	1
3	3	0	1	2

Sometimes a clock is used to
illustrate how such a system
might develop. Here is a 4-
minute clock:

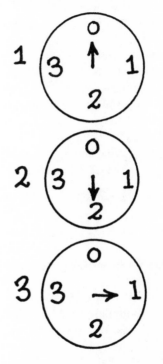

$2 + 3$ means start at 2, then
move the hand 3 units (clockwise). Now the hand points to
1. In this arithmetic, $2 + 3 =$
1. (Check this in the addition
table above.) Mod stands for
modulus or modulo. See *congruent numbers, base of a
numeration system*.

modulo. See *congruent numbers, base of a numeration system.*

modulus (mah'dyou-lus). See *congruent numbers, base of a numeration system.*

Moebius. See *Möbius, August Ferdinand.*

monomial (moh-noh'mee-ul). A monomial can be an *integer:* 7, −3; or a *variable:* x. It can be the product of an integer and variables:

7x, 5xy, 6(−x) (y).

monotony principle. Same as *addition property of inequalities.*

$$\text{IF } a < b$$
$$\text{THEN } a+c < b+c$$

Monte Carlo methods. See *game theory.*

Montessori rods (mon-te-so'ree). Counting sticks used by Countess Maria Montessori, an Italian educator (1870–1952) who believed that children should learn arithmetic using concrete materials. These number rods preceded the *Cuisenaire rods* and *Stern blocks.* Other materials include 10 colored blocks, each graded in size and of a different color; oblong blocks for learning measures of *length;* sets of cylinders of varying

thicknesses; seeds used to represent *points;* rings for *curves;* and tablets for *plane surfaces.* The materials are widely used throughout Europe today.

month. A measurement of time, roughly $\frac{1}{12}$ of a solar year. The lengths of different months were arbitrarily set by various Caesars; they vary from 28 to 31 days and have no actual relation to celestial time. A lunar month of approximately $29\frac{1}{2}$ to 30 days is reckoned by the phases of the moon, but does not "come out even" with the length of the solar year.

more than. See *greater than.*

Moscow papyrus. Perhaps the oldest existing work on mathematics; one of the chief sources of information concerning Egyptian mathematics. Also called the Golenischev. It is now in Moscow.

multinomial. A mathematical expression consisting of 2 or more *terms*.

multiple. Some multiples of 3 are 3, 6, 9, 12, 15 . . . In arithmetic, a multiple of a number is a number which is the *product* of the given number and another *factor*. 24 is a multiple of 2. (24 = 2 × 12). It is also a multiple of 3, 4, 6, 8 **and** other numbers. We say it is a *common multiple* of 2, 3, 4, 6, 8.

$$4 \times 3 = 12$$

FACTORS   MULTIPLE
OF 3 OR
OF 4

multiplicand. A name given to the number that is being multiplied by another number. It is also called a *factor*.

$$23 \leftarrow \text{MULTIPLICAND}$$
$$\times \underline{5} \leftarrow \text{MULTIPLIER}$$

multiplication. A *binary operation* in mathematics. For a pair of *members* of the *set* for which the operation is defined, there is matched a number from the set. For example, to the numbers 3 and 2, there is matched the number 6. 3 × 2 = 6. Each number in the pair of numbers is called a *factor* and the number matched to the pair is called the *product*.

FOR THE SET OF
WHOLE NUMBERS

$$\{1, 2, 3, 4, 5, 6, 7, 8, 9 \ldots\}$$

MEMBERS OF
THE SET   ARE MATCHED TO
ANOTHER MEMBER
OF THE SET

$$2 \cdot 3 = 6$$

FACTORS   PRODUCT

In arithmetic we may think of multiplication of whole numbers in terms of addition. For example, $3 \times 2 = 2 + 2 + 2$. In some newer texts, multiplication is thought of in terms of cross products of sets. Set A has 3 elements. Set A = {a, b, c}. Set B has 2 elements. Set B = {d, e}.

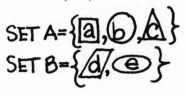

SET A = {a, b, c}
SET B = {d, e}

The cross product of set A and set B is the set of all the pairs of elements from set A and set B. The cross product has 6 elements:

$$A \times B$$

1. (a, d)
2. (a, e)
3. (b, d)
4. (b, e)
5. (c, d)
6. (c, e)

SET A = { a, b, c }

SET B = { d, e }

$A \times B = \{ (a, d)\ (a, e)\ (b, d)$ $(b, e)\ (c, d)\ (c, e) \}$.

See *arithmetic laws, associative property for multiplication, commutative property for multiplication, cross.*

multiplicative identity. In multiplication, the *identity element* is 1 because any number multiplied by 1 gives that number. $27 \times 1 = 27$.

multiplicative inverse. If the product of two numbers is 1, either number is called the multiplicative inverse of the other. For example, since $\frac{2}{5} \times \frac{5}{2} = 1$, $\frac{2}{5}$ is the multiplicative inverse of $\frac{5}{2}$ and $\frac{5}{2}$ is the multiplicative inverse of $\frac{2}{5}$.

multiplier. The *term* or quantity used to multiply another term or quantity. Also called *factor.*

mutually exclusive events. *Disjoint sets,* or events that have no elements in common.

SET A = { 4, 5, 6, 7 }

SET B = { 0, 1, 2 }

DISJOINT SETS ARE MUTUALLY EXCLUSIVE

myria. Prefix meaning 10,000.

N

n. Used to represent any member in a *set.* For example, for all numbers n, $1n = n$.

It is used in discussing the number of *elements* in a set. The

$$\mathsf{SET\ A} = \{\triangle, \square, \bigcirc\}$$

number of elements in set A is 3. This may be written n {A} = 3.

JOHN
NAPIER

Napier, John (nay'pee-er), 1550–1617. A Scottish aristocrat who made many contributions to mathematics, chief among them being the invention of *logarithms*. Although it was a Swiss watchmaker, Jobst Bürgi, who first used *exponents* in logarithms, Napier had the revolutionary idea of working out extremely complex tables for multiplication and division, such as are used in astronomy and engineering. After Napier's death, his friend *Henry Briggs* changed the base to 10, called common logarithms, which are much more easily used in arithmetic. But the so-called Napierian base is often used in the *calculus*.

Napier was responsible for a multiplication device known as *Napier's bones,* for improving the *abacus* and for additions to the field of spherical trigonometry.

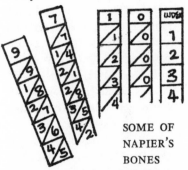

SOME OF
NAPIER'S
BONES

Napier's bones. Sometimes called Napier's rods. A computing device for quick multiplication invented by John *Napier*. It was a forerunner of the *slide rule*.

nappe of a cone (nap). A conical surface (or a pyramidal surface) consists of two nappes which are separated by the *vertex*. See *cone*.

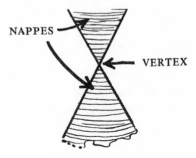

NAPPES

VERTEX

natural logarithm. *Napierian* log-arithm.

natural numbers. The numbers 1, 2, 3, 4 and so on. Also called *counting numbers.* See *numbers.*

nautical mile. A measure of distance used by ships, approximately 6080.27 feet, as opposed to 5280 feet in a land *mile.* See *knot, table p. 218.*

necessary condition. A logical consequence of a given statement. Suppose we say, "If a quadrilateral has a pair of parallel sides, it is a parallelogram." It is necessary that a figure have a pair of parallel sides to be a parallelogram.

needle problem. See *Buffon.*

negation of a statement. Given the statement: George Washington was the first President of the United States. The negation of this statement is: It is not true (or it is false) that George Washington was the first President of the United States. The negation of a proposition or statement, p, is often written ~p, and read: not p.

negative numbers. Numbers less than zero. If a is a *positive number,* and $a + b = 0$, b is called a negative number. The negative numbers are the *addi-tive inverses* of the positive numbers. For example, for a positive number $+6$, there is a negative number -6 such that $+6 + (-6) = 0$.

nest of intervals. A *sequence* of *intervals* such that each one is contained in the preceding one. For example, ⅓ is in the interval between 0 and 1. If that interval is divided into tenths, ⅓ will lie between .3 and .4. This interval may be divided again and again. Each interval, lying within the interval used before, gives it the name "nest."

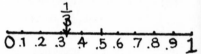

net. See *development* of a geometric solid figure.

net price. The price of an item after deductions have been made for charges, expenses, loss, etc.

net weight. The actual weight of an object without its container. See *gross weight.*

NET WEIGHT

network. In *topology,* the diagram
of a problem. See *arcs.*

THE KÖNIGSBERG BRIDGES
LOOKED LIKE THIS

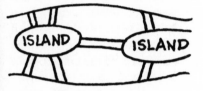

THE NETWORK OF THE
PROBLEM LOOKED LIKE
THIS

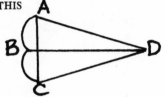

Newton, Sir Isaac, 1642–1727.
An English mathematician and
physicist, sometimes called the
greatest genius who ever lived.
He established his 3 famous

SIR ISAAC
NEWTON

laws of motion:
1. A body at rest tends to remain at rest and a body in
motion tends to remain in
motion (inertia).
2. A change in motion is in
proportion to the force causing
the change, and occurs in the
direction in which the force is
moving (momentum).
3. For every action, there is an
equal and opposite reaction.
Newton also discovered the
universal law of gravitation.
In optics, the study of both
light and vision, he demonstrated that white light is a
combination of all the other
colors.
In pure mathematics, he investigated the *binomial theorem*
for negative and fractional
values, and wrote many papers
on algebra and equations.
One of Newton's chief contributions was the invention of
the *calculus,* which he called
the "method of fluxions." For
many years argument raged
over whether he or *Leibniz*
founded this new field. It is
now believed that both men
worked independently, and although the notation system of
Leibniz is preferred, many of
the concepts are Newton's.

Nichomachus (nih-koh′ma-kus),
about the first century A.D.

A Roman mathematician who
published a book on arithmetic which for a thousand
years was the standard. The
book was concerned with the
properties of numbers and
their ratios. *Boethius,* whose
textbook was used widely in
the Middle Ages, based his
work on that of Nichomachus.

nilpotent (nil′poh-tent). An element that has a *power* equal to
zero. In ordinary arithmetic,
zero itself is the only nilpotent
element, but this is not always
so in other forms of mathematics.

nines, casting out. A way of checking an addition problem by
adding the remainders of each
addend and the remainder of
the *sum* when the multiples of
9 are subtracted. The sum of
the remainder should be equal
to the sum. The final sums
must be one-digit numbers.

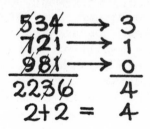

nomograph (sometimes called
nomogram). A *graph* or diagram, usually consisting of 3
scales graduated for different
variables, so that when a line
segment connects points on any
2, the related value is read
where the line intersects the
third scale. In the graph below,
$A + B = C$.

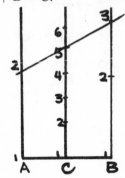

A perpetual calendar is a
nomograph. So is a height-
weight chart. Engineering nom-
ographs are much more complicated. See *slide rule.*

nonagon. A nine-sided *polygon.*

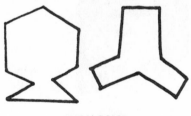

NONAGONS

noncollinear points (non-koh-lin′ ee-uhr). If *points* A, B and C are three points not all on the same *line,* then points A, B and C are noncollinear. See *collinear.*

non-Euclidean geometry. See *geometry, non-Euclidean.*

non-negative numbers. The *set* of *positive numbers* and zero.

nonpositional notation. A *numeration system* like the *Egyptian* that does not use *place value* for expressing numbers. For example,

∩∩||| means $10 + 10 + 1 + 1 + 1$ or 23. Each symbol has a value, but the value does not depend on its position in the numeral.

nonpositive numbers. The *set* of *negative numbers* and zero.

nonsimple closed curve. A *closed curve* which crosses itself in at least one place.

norm. In *statistics,* a term meaning normal or average. See *central tendency, measures of.*

normal. In *plane geometry,* being at right angles or *perpendicular.*

normal curve of distribution. See *bell-shaped curve.*

NORMAL CURVE
OF DISTRIBUTION

notation, system of. In mathematics, a system of symbols or numerals representing numbers. See *Babylonian, Egyptian, Hindu-Arabic, Mayan numeration system.* Also *binary system, base.*

0,1,2,3,4,5,6,7,8,9
HINDU-ARABIC SYMBOLS

not equal to. 4 is not equal to 5. This may be written $4 \neq 5$.

null set. Empty *set;* one with no *members.* A symbol for the null set is { } or ϕ.

number. A concept of quantity.
Natural numbers,
{1, 2, 3, 4, . . .}
Whole numbers,
{0, 1, 2, 3, 4, . . .}
Integers,
{−3, −2, −1, 0, +1, +2, +3, . . .}
There is also the *set* of *rational numbers.* One example is ⅘. There are sets of other numbers, such as *irrational numbers, real numbers* and *complex numbers.*

number frame. A shape used for a *placeholder* in a *number sentence.*

$$2 + \square = 16$$

NUMBER FRAMES

$$8 < 2 + \triangle$$

See *equation, inequality.*

number line. A line on which points are associated with numbers in a *one-to-one* correspondence is called a number line. See *zero, positive numbers, negative numbers.*

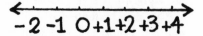

PART OF THE
NUMBER LINE

number sentence. A mathematical *sentence* which expresses a complete thought. Some examples of number sentences are

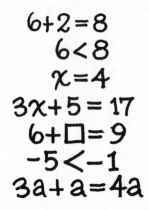

numbers, theory of. A branch of *pure mathematics* concerned generally with the *properties* and relationships of *integers.* In primitive times, and even in the early Greek and Chinese civilizations, numbers were thought to have certain magic properties.

4 , 30 , 101

NUMERALS

numeral. A symbol or name for a number.
numeration. See *notation, systems of.*

numerator. In $\frac{6}{7}$, 6 is the numerator. See *denominator*.

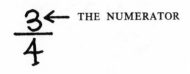

3 ← THE NUMERATOR
4

O

O. O is used to name a point as the center of a circle.

We say circle O. It is the abbreviation for *origin*.

A *digit* in the *Hindu-Arabic numeration system,* zero.

0 is the numeral for the number of *elements* in the *empty set*.

oblate (ob'late). Flattened. The earth is an oblate *sphere* because it is slightly flattened at both poles.

oblique. Slanting; a line that is neither horizontal nor vertical.

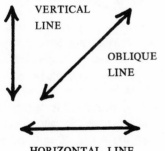

VERTICAL
LINE

OBLIQUE
LINE

HORIZONTAL LINE

oblique angle. Any acute or obtuse *angle,* but not a right angle.

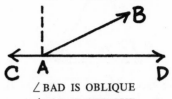

∠BAD IS OBLIQUE
∠CAB IS OBLIQUE

oblique circular cone. A *cone* in which the *axis* is not *perpendicular* to the plane of the *base*.

OBLIQUE CIRCULAR CONE

oblique circular cylinder. A *cylinder* in which the planes of the bases are oblique to elements of the cylinder.

OBLIQUE
CIRCULAR
CYLINDER

oblique prism. A *prism* in which *lateral* edges are not *perpendicular* to the bases.

OBLIQUE
PRISM

oblique triangle. A triangle that does not contain a *right angle*.

obtuse angle. Any angle whose measure is more than 90° and less than 180°.

OBTUSE ANGLE

obtuse triangle. A triangle having one *obtuse angle*.

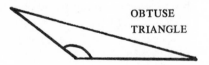

OBTUSE TRIANGLE

occurrence of an event. If you toss a coin and it falls heads, an *event* has occurred. If it falls tails, that is an event too.

octagon. A *polygon* having 8 sides.

OCTAHEDRON

octahedron (ok'ta-heed'run). A *polygon* having 8 faces.

octal numeration system. A *base eight* system. See *notation, system of*.

octant (ok'tant). In plane geometry, one-eighth of a circle. In space or spherical geometry, one of the eight parts into which the *coordinate planes* divide the space.

OCTANT

odd number. Any *natural number* that does not have 2 as a *factor,* or cannot be divided by 2 with zero remainder. Any odd number can be written $2n + 1$ where n is a whole number. 1, 3, 5 and 7 are some examples of odd numbers.

odds. The ratio between the probability of an event occurring and the probability of an event not occurring is called the odds of the event occurring. To throw a 7 with dice, there are 6 ways in which the event can occur and 30 ways in which it cannot occur. The odds in favor of the event occurring are

$$\frac{\frac{6}{36}}{\frac{30}{36}} = \frac{6}{30} = \frac{1}{5} \text{ or } 1 \text{ to } 5.$$

ohm. A unit of measure of electrical resistance in a wire.

Omar Khayyam, c. A.D. 1100. A Persian poet, astronomer and mathematician. Although he is best known in the Western world for his poem, "The Rubaiyat," he wrote many works on the geometry of *Euclid,* on algebra, and on astronomy. His *sequence* of *coefficients,* arranged in the form of a triangular number, led to the *probability triangle* of *Pascal.* He is known for his geometric solution of *cubic equations.* See also *Precious Mirror of the Four Elements.*

one. A *cardinal number,* the smallest member of the *set* of *natural numbers* or counting numbers. It is associated with a point which is one unit length to the right of zero on the *number line.*

one dimensional. Usually refers to a figure having length only, such as a *line segment.*

one-sided surface. See *Möbius strip, topology.*

one-to-one correspondence. When every *element* in one *set* can be matched with one and only one element in another set and every element in the second set can be matched with one and only one element of the first set, there is a one-to-one relationship between the sets.

SET A = {△, ○, ◉, x}

SET B = {1, 2, 3, 4}

open curve. A *curve* in which the *endpoints* do not meet.

OPEN CURVES

OPEN INTERVAL
(NUMBERS GREATER THAN
−1 AND LESS THAN +2)

open interval. See *interval.*

open sentence. A *mathematical sentence* that includes a *variable* representing any number from a set of numbers. The sentence may be either an *equation* or an *inequality,* $3x + 2 = 18$ is an open sentence. See *placeholder, number frame.*

operation. *Multiplication* and *addition* are *binary operations.* Any *ordered pair* of a *set* is matched with another member of the set. For example, addition matches 5 with $(2, 3)$. $2 + 3 = 5$. Multiplication matches 6 with $(2, 3)$. $2 \times 3 = 6$. *Subtraction* and *division* are not completely defined for the set of *whole numbers.* These operations are not closed or do not have *closure* for the set of whole numbers. For example, under subtraction, the pair of numbers $(3, 5)$ has no number matched with it because the set of whole numbers does not include negative numbers, but $(5, 3)$ has the number 2 matched with it, $5 - 3 = 2$. Division is not closed either.

However, subtraction on the set of *real numbers* $(3, 5)$ has −2 matched with it, and division matches 3/5 with $(3, 5)$. See *arithmetic operation, intersection, numbers, union.*

opposite. See *additive inverse.*

opposite vertical angles. In the picture, angles 1 and 3 are a pair of opposite vertical angles.

So are angles 2 and 4. In *parallelogram* ABCD, ∠ A and ∠ C are called opposite angles.

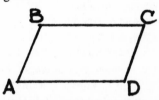

or. A *connective.* A *compound sentence* with "or" is called a disjunctive sentence. "Or" connects two clauses. "John is at home or he is at the movies," is an example·of a disjunctive sentence. It is true if either of its clauses is true or if both of them are true. The symbol for "or" used in some books is $\vee$.

ordered pair. Two numbers in a certain order. The pair $(3, 5)$ is not the same as the pair $(5, 3)$. See *Cartesian coordinates*.

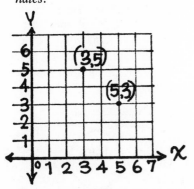

order on a number line. The *point* associated with the smaller number is to the left of the point associated with the larger number. -1 is greater than -3.

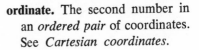

order properties of the real numbers. For all real numbers a, b, c, d:
1. If $a < b$,
then $a + c < b + c$.
2. If $a > b$ and $c > 0$, then $ac > bc$.

3. If $a < b$ and $b < c$, then $a < c$.
4. If $a > b$ and $c < 0$, then $ac < bc$.
5. Exactly one of the following can be true: $a = b$, or $a < b$, or $a > b$.

ordinal numbers. Numbers that specify order or position of a *member* of a *set*. First, second, third, are ordinal numbers related to the *cardinal* numbers one, two, three.

FIRST   SECOND   THIRD

ordinate. The second number in an *ordered pair* of coordinates. See *Cartesian coordinates*.

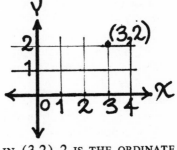

IN $(3,2)$ 2 IS THE ORDINATE
3 IS THE ABSCISSA

Oresme, Nicole, 1323–1382. Oresme seems to have pre-dated *Descartes* in locating points with coordinates. However, the essential system was developed by Descartes and *Fermat*.

origin. The point where the *x-axis* and *y-axis* intersect. The *ordered pair* given to the origin is (0, 0). See *Cartesian coordinates*.

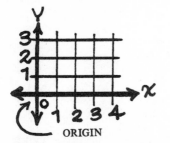

ORIGIN

Oughtred, William, 1575–1660. An English mathematician who introduced the symbol × for multiplication and : for proportion. He described a circular slide rule in his book "Circles of Proportion," in 1632, and a year later introduced a rectangular logarithmic slide rule.

ounce. A unit of weight; $\frac{1}{16}$ of a pound in *avoirdupois weight,* $\frac{1}{12}$ of a pound in *apothecaries' weight,* approximately 28.35 grams. See *table p. 216.*

overhead. Operating expenses in a business, such as rent, taxes, etc.

overlapping sets. Two or more *sets* that have one or more *elements* or members in common. For instance, if set A is all the boys in your classroom, and set B is all the boys in your club, and you and John are in both sets, the sets would be overlapping. See *intersection of sets.*

OVERLAPPING SETS

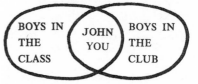

P

P. P is used to designate a *point.*

p. The letter that forms the first part of the *conditional open sentence,* "if p then q," written p → q.

Pappus, c. A.D. 300. A geometrician who lived and taught in Alexandria. Some of his work has been lost. Of the 8 books known to have existed, probably the first was on arithmetic, the next four were on geometry, the sixth dealt with astronomy, the seventh with analysis and conics and the eighth with mechanics. He presented many brilliant theorems, but he lived at a time when there was little interest in them.

parabola (pa-rab′uh-la). A curve that can be obtained by cutting a right circular *cone* by a *plane* parallel to one of the elements. A parabola may also be described as the *locus,* or path of a point which moves so that it remains equidistant from a fixed point and a fixed line.

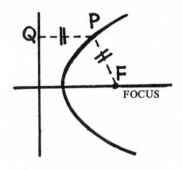

FIXED LINE
(DIRECTRIX)

PQ IS ALWAYS EQUAL TO PF

paradox. An argument that appears to show that something which is "obviously" false is true. See *Zeno.*

parallelepiped (pa-ruh-lel-ih-pie′ped). A *prism* whose bases are parallelograms.

PARABOLA

PARALLELEPIPED

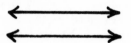

parallel lines. Two or more lines in the same *plane* that do not intersect. See *Euclid's 5th postulate; geometry, Euclidean; geometry, non-Euclidean.*

parallelogram. A *quadrilateral* in which both pairs of opposite sides are parallel.

PARALLELOGRAMS

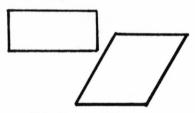

parallel planes. Two *planes* which do not intersect.

PARALLEL PLANES

parallel postulate. See *Euclid's parallel postulate.*

parallels on maps. Lines of *latitude* that run parallel to the *equator.*

parameter. An arbitrary *constant.* A *variable* in an algebraic expression that temporarily assumes the properties of a constant. For example, in y = mx + b, m and b are parameters if either is treated as a constant in a *family of lines.*

parentheses. A grouping symbol ( ). If no rule for the order of operations has been agreed upon, $3 \times 2 + 4$ may mean 10 or it may mean 18. When we agree to the rule of first multiplication and then addition, $3 \times 2 + 4 = 10$. If we want addition first we use parentheses and write $3 \times (2 + 4)$, which equals 18.

parity of integers. Two integers have the same parity if they are both odd or both even. Integers are of opposite or different parity if one is odd and the other is even.

parsec. In measuring celestial bodies, 206,000 astronomical units or 3.26 light years.

partial product. In multiplication:

$$\begin{array}{r} 235 \\ \times\ 21 \\ \hline 235 \\ 4700 \\ \hline 4935 \end{array}$$

235 PARTIAL PRODUCT
4700 PARTIAL PRODUCT
4935 PRODUCT

BLAISE
PASCAL

Pascal, Blaise (pas-kal′), 1623–1662. A French mathematician who, at 16, was already renowned for his work on *conic sections*. He later became interested in projective geometry, which had been started by *Desargues*. He invented a practical calculating machine that was too expensive to produce. After that, because of a problem sent to him by his friend *de Méré,* he began work on the *probability* theory.

Pascal's triangle. See *probability triangle*.

pathological curves. *Curves* having unusual properties. Among them is the snowflake curve, which can be drawn on a piece of paper, but which has an *infinite perimeter*. It starts with an *equilateral triangle*. Next each side is trisected and an

SNOWFLAKE CURVE

equilateral triangle constructed on each. This is repeated. Another pathological curve is the crisscross curve, which crosses itself at every one of its points.

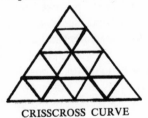

CRISSCROSS CURVE

patterns. Mathematics is a study of patterns. Patterns emerge from sets of statements. For example, from this set of statements, is it reasonable to suppose that the product of a positive number and a negative number is negative?

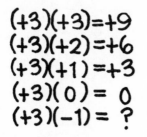

$$(+3)(+3)=+9$$
$$(+3)(+2)=+6$$
$$(+3)(+1)=+3$$
$$(+3)(0)= 0$$
$$(+3)(-1)= ?$$

Peano's five axioms. The five axioms of *positive integers,* as described by Giuseppe Peano, Italian mathematician of the late 19th century:
1. There is a positive integer 1.
2. Every positive integer has a *unique* positive integer as its *successor.*
3. No positive integer has 1 as its successor.
4. Distinct positive integers have distinct successors.
5. If a statement holds for the positive integer 1, and if, whenever it holds for a positive integer, it also holds for that integer's successor, then the statement holds for all positive integers.
This last axiom is the famous "principle of mathematical induction."

peck. A measure of capacity, 4 quarts. See *table p. 251.*

penny. A coin. In the United States $\frac{1}{100}$ of a dollar.

pennyweight. In *Troy weight,* 24 grains. See *table p. 216.*

pentagon. A *polygon* having 5 sides.

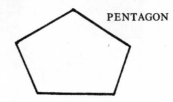

PENTAGON

percent. A *ratio* in which the *denominator* is 100. The symbol for percent is %. For example, $\frac{1}{4}$ is $\frac{25}{100}$, .25 or 25%. All name the same number.

percentage. A number. 10% of 70 is 7. The percentage is 7, the *base* is 70 and the *rate* is 10%.

percentile. The position in a set of *scores* given in terms of percent of scores below or above

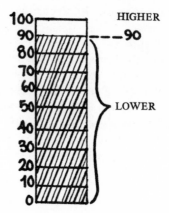

this position. For example, a percentile score of 90 means that only 10% of the scores were higher and 90% of the scores were lower in the set of scores.

percent of error. The *relative error* of a measurement expressed as a percent. For example, if we use a ruler scaled in inches, a measurement of 5″ has a greatest possible error of .5″. The relative error is .5/5 or .10. The percent of error is 10%.

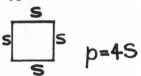

10% PERCENT OF ERROR

perfect number. An *integer* which is equal to the sum of all its *factors* except the number itself. 6 is a perfect number because $1 + 2 + 3 = 6$.

perfect square. A number or expression which can be stated as the *product* of two equal *factors*. 9 is a perfect square because $9 = 3 \times 3$.

perimeter of a polygon. The sum of the lengths of the sides of the *polygon*.

$$p = 4s$$

period. To make reading numerals easier, sets of *digits* are set off by commas. For example, 1,234,567. Each set is called a period. 1 is in the millions period; 234 is in the thousands period; 567 is in the unit period. See *decimal point*.

periodic decimals. See *decimals, repeating*.

period of interest. The length of time over which interest is figured. It might be a year, 6 months, 3 months or so on.

permutation. An arrangement. If there are three books, A, B and C, they can be arranged in piles of 3 in 6 different ways: ABC, ACB, BAC, BCA, CAB, CBA. The order of the elements is important in permutations. In *combinations,*

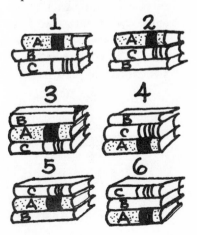

order is not important. There is only one combination of books A, B and C.

perpendicular bisector. A line or line segment that is perpendicular to a line segment and divides it into two equal parts.

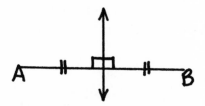

perpendicular lines. Two lines are perpendicular (⊥) to each other if they form two equal adjacent angles with each other. The equal adjacent angles are called *right angles*.

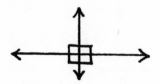

PERPENDICULAR LINES

perpetual calendar. A *nomograph* that tells on one chart the day on which any given date will fall in any year.

pi (pie). An *irrational number* for which the symbol is π. The *ratio* of the *circumference* to the *diameter* of any circle is $C/D = \pi$. A rational approximation for π is $22/7$ or 3.14; carried further, it is 3.14159+. Pi is a *nonterminating, nonrepeating decimal*. See *Ludolphian number*.

pie chart. See *graph*.

pint. A unit of liquid measure; $\frac{1}{2}$ of a *quart*. See *table p. 218*.

placeholder. A *variable*. In the mathematical sentence, $\square + 3 = 5$, $\square$ is the symbol that holds the place for an element from a given set. If $\square$ holds the place for 2, then $\square + 3 = 5$ becomes $2 + 3 = 5$. In the higher grades, a letter such as x is used instead of $\square$.

MANY SYMBOLS MAY BE USED AS PLACEHOLDERS

$$\square + 3 = 5$$
$$4 - \triangle = 0$$
$$2x = 8$$
$$3y + 4 = 13$$

place value. In a numeral such as 3452 written in the *Hindu-Arabic system,* the *digit* 3 represents the number 3×1000. The number 1000 is the *place value* of the position occupied by the digit 3 in the numeral 3452. Place values are numbers assigned to positions in a numeral.

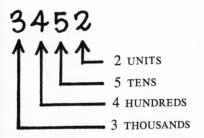

plane. A flat *surface.* A straight line joining any two points in the surface lies entirely in the surface. The face of a chalk board represents part of a plane. A plane extends infinitely in all directions.

plane figures. Any *set* of *points* in a *plane.* Some common plane figures are angles, triangles and circles.

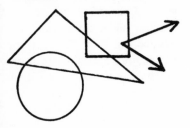

plane geometry. See *geometry, plane.*

plane of symmetry. Two points are *symmetric* to a *plane* if the plane is the *perpendicular bisector* of the line segment joining the points. A geometric figure is symmetric with respect to a plane if for every point on the figure, there is another point so that the two points are symmetric with respect to the plane.

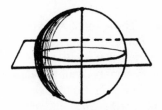

plane region. The interior of a *simple closed curve.* The region usually does not include its boundary.

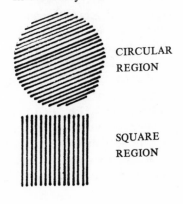

CIRCULAR REGION

SQUARE REGION

planimeter. An instrument used for finding the area of a plane figure, by guiding a tracing device along its perimeter.

PLATO

Plato, 429–347 B.C. An Athenian teacher and pupil of Socrates who felt that mathematics was the beginning of all knowledge, as shown in his *Quadrivium*. Like *Pythagoras,* he felt that the secret of the universe was in number and form.

Over the entrance to his school were the words: "Let none ignorant of geometry enter my door." He is thought to have been responsible for the system of definitions, *postulates* and *axioms,* used in constructing geometric proofs.

plotting a curve. Locating *points* from *coordinates* and connecting these points with a curve that approximates or resembles the actual curve which pictures the relationship existing between *variables*.

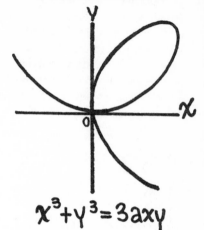

$$x^3 + y^3 = 3axy$$

plumb line. A device made of a string with a weight attached. The force of gravity pulls the string straight down.

The plumb line sometimes refers to the line in which the string hangs and sometimes to the string itself.

plus. The name of the symbol for the operation of addition. The symbol is $+$.

Poincaré, Jules Henri (pwan-ka-ray'), 1854–1912. A French mathematician and physicist who published hundreds of articles on mathematics. He pointed out that the basis for the choice of *axioms* for a geometry should be convenience

155   **polygon**

JULES HENRI
POINCARÉ

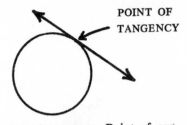

POINT OF
TANGENCY

and usefulness. He said it was possible to discuss the *properties* of a geometry which could not be "seen" by the senses. He did work in elliptical functions, celestial mechanics and the calculus of probabilities. His work prepared the way for the acceptance of the revolutionary theories of Planck and Einstein.

point. An *undefined term* in geometry. It has position, but no dimensions, and is usually represented by a dot to mark a location. Its position is usually defined by *coordinates*.

point of tangency. Point of contact. The point at which a *tangent* touches a circle.

point-set theory. A study of properties preserved under all one-to-one *correspondence*.

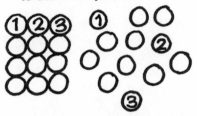

POINTS REMAIN IN ONE-TO-ONE CORRESPONDENCE EVEN THOUGH THEIR ORDER CHANGES

polygon. A simple *closed curve* which is the union of *line segments*.

POLYGONS

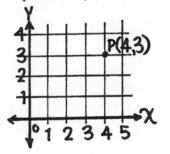

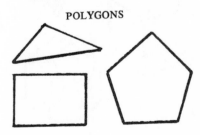

polyhedral angle. A figure formed by the lateral *faces* of a *polyhedron,* which have a common *vertex.*

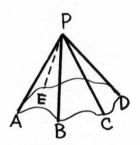

POLYHEDRAL ANGLE P

polyhedron. A solid formed by portions of plane surfaces which are called the *faces.*

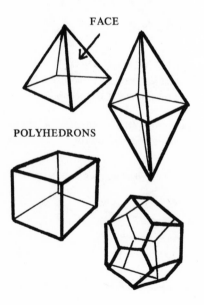

polynomial (pol′ih-no′mi-al). A *monomial* or the algebraic sum of monomials:

POLYNOMIALS

$$5y; \quad 6a-2b;$$
$$2x^2+3x+7$$

NOT POLYNOMIALS

$$\frac{3x}{y}; \quad \frac{4(x-y)}{x}$$

polynomial form of numerals. The expanded form of a numeral in which the *place value* of the digits is used. $6352 = 6 \times 10^3 + 3 \times 10^2 + 5 \times 10^1 + 2.$ See *expanded notation.*

Poncelet, Jean Victor (pon-si-lay′), 1788–1867. A French mathematician. While imprisoned during the French retreat from Moscow, he wrote a famous textbook on modern geometry. He also established the chief properties of conic sections, and expanded the theory of polygons. He is best remembered for his theory on the continuity of numbers.

position. See *place value, topology.*

positive error. See *error.*

positive integers. *Integers* greater than zero. See *Peano's five axioms.*

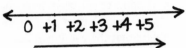

POSITIVE NUMBERS

positive numbers. *Numbers* associated with points on a number line to the right of the zero point.

possible error. In any measurement, it is $\frac{1}{2}$ of the smallest unit of measure used. If a ruler is marked off in $\frac{1}{8}$'s, the *greatest possible error* with this ruler is $\frac{1}{16}''$.

postulate. A statement in mathematics that is assumed to be true without proof. Postulates are sometimes called *assumptions* or *axioms*.

postulates of Euclid. See *Euclid*.

pound. A measure of avoirdupois weight; 16 ounces. See *table p. 216*.
A British unit of money.

power. An expression such as 2^3 means $2 \times 2 \times 2$. 2^3 is called a power. It is the third power of 2 and it is equal to 8. In general, a^n is a number and is called the nth power of a. See *exponent*.

Precious Mirror of the Four Elements. A *triangular number* sequence on which the *probability triangle* of *Pascal* was probably based. It was composed about A.D. 1300 by the Chinese mathematician Chushi Kei, and is related to the so-called coefficients of *Omar Khayyam*.

precision of measurement. The size of the units determines the precision. The smaller the unit the more precise the measurement. See *true length, measured length*.

premise. A proposition in a proof that leads to a conclusion.

prime factor. A *factor* of a number when the factor itself is a *prime number*.

$$42 = 2 \times 3 \times 7$$

PRIME FACTORS

prime number. A *natural number* that has no other factors except 1 and itself. 2, 3, 5, 7, 11, 13, 17, 19, 23 . . . are prime numbers. (1 is usually not included in the set of prime numbers.) See *sieve of Eratosthenes, composite number*.

principal. The amount of money in a savings account earning a certain rate of *interest*. Also the amount of money borrowed from a lending institution at a certain interest.

principal axis. See *major axis*.

principal square root. Every positive *real number* has two *square roots*. One is positive and the other is negative. The positive square root is called the principal square root. The principal square root is denoted by $\sqrt{}$. The principal square root of 9 is $\sqrt{9}$ or 3.

principle, mathematical. A rule or law which is either assumed or proved. It may state a relationship between numbers. For example, for all numbers a and b, $a + b = b + a$ is called the *commutative principle* (or property) of addition.

prism. A *polyhedron* with two *congruent* and *parallel faces* called the bases.

PRISM

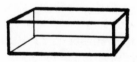

probability. A branch of mathematics. If in a single trial, an *event* can occur in s ways, and fail to occur in f ways, and the likelihood of all ways happening is equal, then the probability that the event will occur is $p = \dfrac{s}{(s + f)}$. If in a toss of a coin, heads can occur in 1 way and fail in 1 way, the probability that a head will occur in 1 trial is $p = \dfrac{1}{(1 + 1)}$ or $\frac{1}{2}$. The probability of an event ranges from 0 to 1. If the probability of an event occuring is 1, the event is certain. If the probability of an event occurring is 0, the event certainly will not occur.

probability triangle (or Pascal triangle). An *array* in triangle form. The numbers in the array form the *coefficients* of the *expansion* $(a + b)^n$ for n, a whole number. The triangle is used in probability theory. The first 6 rows look like this:

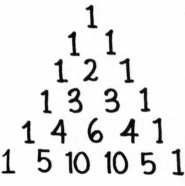

proceeds. The amount of money received in a business transaction.

product. The result of a *binary operation* called multiplication of two numbers or *factors*.

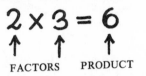

FACTORS   PRODUCT

profit. The difference between the cost plus expenses and the sale price of an item.

progression. See *arithmetic progression, geometric progression, number sequence.*

project (proh-ject′). To transform the *points* of one figure into those of another by any *correspondence* between points. See *geometry, projective.*

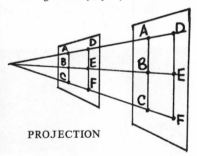

PROJECTION

promissory note. A written statement which is a promise to pay a stated amount of money on a given date.

proof. The logical argument, usually a set of statements and reasons, to establish the truth of a *proposition.* See *conclusion.*

proper fraction. A *fraction* with the numerator smaller than the denominator. ¾ and ⅞ are proper fractions.

proper subset. If every *element* of *set* B is also an element of set A, and there is at least one element in set A that is not in set B, we say that set B is a proper subset of set A.
If set A = {a, b, c, d, e } then a proper subset of A is
set B = {a, b, c }. See *subset, complementary set.*

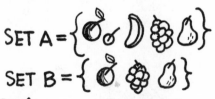

BcA   PROPER SUBSET

property. A characteristic. See *principle, mathematical.*

proportion. A statement of *equality* between two *ratios.* For example, ³⁄₆ = ½;
or 3:6 = 1:2, read: 3 is to 6 as 1 is to 2. See *means, extremes.*

proportion, in art. The mathematical relationship between the parts in a painting or sculpture and the actual sizes and relationships of the things themselves. Many artists deliberately distort these relationships to emphasize a point of view. See *golden section.*

proposition. An idea to which "true" or "false" is associated, but not both. A *statement* is an expression of a proposition. In geometry a proposition is called a *theorem* when it is proved.

propositions of Euclid. The statements set forth in the *Elements* of Euclid which form the basis for Euclidean geometry. See *Euclid's 5th postulate.*

protractor. An instrument used to measure angles.

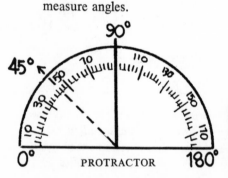

PROTRACTOR

pseudosphere (sue'doh-sfeer). Invented by *Beltrami* and sometimes called a "double trumpet" surface. The geometry of *Lobachevski* and *Bolyai*

PSEUDOSPHERE

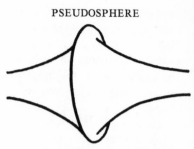

was based on the pseudosphere.

Ptolemy (tol'eh-mee), c. A.D. 100–168. A Greek mathematician, astronomer and geographer who was born in Egypt. His work, the "Almagest," shows that he was a great geometrician. He tried to prove *Euclid's 5th postulate.* His theory of the universe, accepted until the time of *Copernicus* and *Galileo,* stated that heavenly bodies revolve around the earth. He gave a value of π as approximately 3.1416.

PTOLEMY

punch card. A card on which certain information is written by the piercing of holes in various parts of the card.

pure mathematics. The study of mathematical systems. Pure mathematics does not concern itself with solving practical problems of business or science.

PYTHAGORAS

Pythagoras (pih-thag'oh-ras), c. 582–507 B.C. A Greek philosopher and geometrician and the founder of the Pythagorean school or brotherhood. Its members took an oath to keep the teachings secret and hold the same beliefs. The regular *solids,* classified by Pythagoras, are sometimes still called Pythagorean solids. Members of the Pythagorean school were much concerned with the relationships of whole numbers, and felt that they were mystical. Probably the best-known geometric theorem is called the *Pythagorean theorem.*

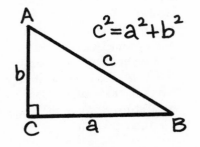

$$c^2 = a^2 + b^2$$

Pythagorean theorem. This states that for any right triangle, the sum of the square of the lengths of the sides or legs is equal to the square of the length of the hypotenuse.

pyramid. A solid figure that has a *polygonal region* for a base and whose lateral faces are triangle regions.

PYRAMIDS

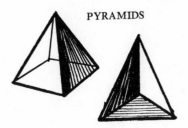

pyramid number. A number in the shape of a pyramid, first discovered by the Greeks, who were interested in the shapes of numbers. It is related to a *triangular number,* but has a third dimension, just as a *square number* is related to a cube number.

pyramid, truncated. The portion of a pyramid included between its *base* and any plane section, cutting all the faces except the base. If the cutting plane is parallel to the base, the shape is called a frustum.

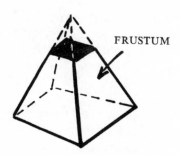

FRUSTUM

the form "if p then q" is called a *conditional;* q is called the *conclusion.*

quadrangle, simple. A plane figure having four points, no three of which are *collinear,* and *line segments* connecting them in order. See *quadrilateral.*

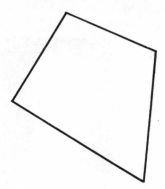

quadrantal angle. An angle in which the *terminal side* coin-

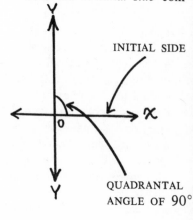

INITIAL SIDE

QUADRANTAL
ANGLE OF 90°

Q

q. The letter that follows p in the statement "if p then q," written: $p \rightarrow q$. A sentence of

cides with one of the axes. It is understood that the initial side is on the x-axis. The measures of the quadrantal angle are 0°, 90°, 180°, 270° and so on.

quadrant of the coordinate plane.
The *x-axis* and the *y-axis* divide the *coordinate plane* into four regions, each called a quadrant. The quadrants are numbered counterclockwise, starting with the upper-right quadrant. Points on the axes are not in the quadrants.

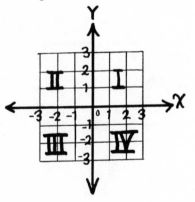

QUADRANTS OF THE
COORDINATE PLANE

quadratic equation. An *equation* of second *degree*. Equations of the form $ax^2 + bx + c = 0$, where a, b, c are *real numbers* and $a \neq 0$, are called quadratic equations.

GRAPHS OF QUADRATIC EQUATIONS
FORM CONIC SECTIONS

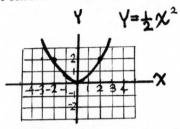

quadratic formula. A formula used to compute the *roots* of a *quadratic equation* in the form $ax^2 + bx + c = 0$ and $a \neq 0$. The formula is usually written:

$$x = \frac{-b \pm \sqrt{b^2 - 4ac}}{2a}$$

quadrature. The process of finding a square equal in area to another given surface, usually a circle or other curved surface. See *circle, squaring the.*

quadrilateral. A *polygon* having four sides. See *parallelogram, rectangle, square, trapezoid.*

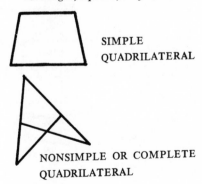

SIMPLE
QUADRILATERAL

NONSIMPLE OR COMPLETE
QUADRILATERAL

Quadrivium of Mathematics
(kwad-riv'ee-um). Plato's
method of showing the relationship of all knowledge to
mathematics, and one of the

first classifications of mathematics.

This is probably based on the
Quadrivium of *Pythagoras*,

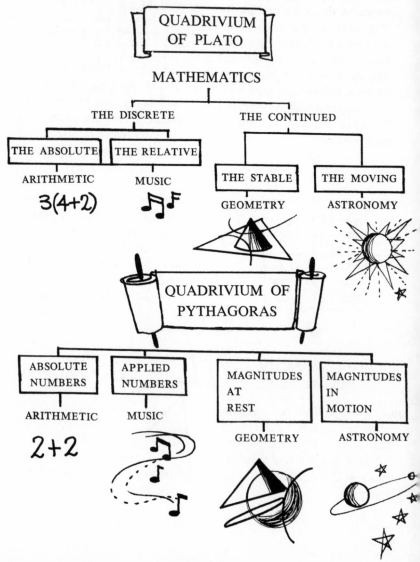

quantity. An amount, or a number, or an expression which takes on value.

quart. A measure of capacity. 2 pints, 0.946 liters. See *table p. 218.*

quarter. One of four equal parts into which something is divided. Also, the common term used in the United States and Canada for the coin worth ¼ of a dollar, or approximately 25 cents.

quartic equation. An *equation* of the fourth *degree.*

quartile. A set of *scores* can be divided into four equal parts. The *median* divides the scores into a lower and an upper half. The median is sometimes called the second quartile. The measure which divides the lower half into two equal parts is called the first quartile, and that which divides the upper half is the third quartile. The 25th, 50th and 75th *percentiles* are the 1st, 2nd and 3rd quartiles.

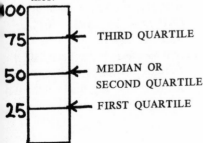

THIRD QUARTILE

MEDIAN OR
SECOND QUARTILE

FIRST QUARTILE

quaternions (kwa-ter'nee-onz). One of the basic laws of number systems is the *commutative property* of multiplication, for example, $6 \times 5 = 5 \times 6$. In the 1830s and 1840s, *Hamilton* freed algebra from centuries of tradition by setting up a system, quaternions, in which the commutative property of multiplication does not apply: $a \times b \neq b \times a$. He thus made possible many new algebras, just as freedom from thinking strictly in terms of *Euclidean geometry* made the *non-Euclidean geometries* possible. Quaternions were the first of many kinds of *hypercomplex numbers.*

Quetelet, Lambert Adolphe (kay' te-lay'), 1796–1874. A Belgian teacher of mathematics and science. He inspired and superintended the building of the royal observatory at Brussels and became its director. He planned a census in 1829. Collecting figures on the influence of sex, age, education, etc., on crimes, he was amazed at the accuracy of predictions which were possible. His studies of *statistics* and *probability* showed that human traits could be predicted. This was the first time that conclusions relative to society were drawn from statistics.

quinary system of numeration (kwy'neh-ree). A numeration system using base five. See *base five system*.

$$0, 1, 2, 3, 4$$

A QUINARY SYSTEM
HAS FIVE NUMERALS

quindecagon. A *polygon* with 15 sides.

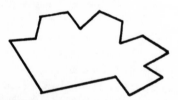

quintal. In the metric system, a unit of weight equal to 100 *kilograms*. See *table p. 219*.

quintic equation. An equation of the fifth *degree*.

quintunx. An arrangement of five objects in a square, or rectangle, one at each corner and one in the middle.

quire (kwyr). A set of 24 sheets of paper of equal size.

quotient. The name commonly given to the result when one number is divided by another. For example, 5 is the quotient resulting from the *division* of 10 by 2. In general, the term is used as follows:

$$9 \div 2 \text{ or } \frac{9}{2} \text{ or } 2\overline{)9}$$

MEANS

$$9 = \square \times 2 + \triangle$$

QUOTIENT   REMAINDER

Since $9 = 4 \times 2 + 1$, 4 is the quotient and 1 is the remainder.

R

R. Used to designate the set of *real numbers*.

r. Abbreviation for *radius, rate*. It is also used as a *variable* in such *formulas* as the distance formula, d = rt.

radian measure. Sometimes called *circular measure*. The unit is a radian, or any angle that, if placed with its *vertex* at the

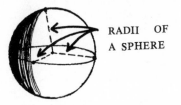

1 RADIAN

center of a circle, intercepts an *arc* equal to the length of the *radius* of the circle. The intercepted arc is the same length as the radius. Radian measure is too large for practical measurements like surveying, but is very useful in advanced mathematics.

radical. An expression consisting of a phrase and a radical sign over it is called a radical. Expressions such as $\sqrt{36}$, $\sqrt[3]{64}$, $\sqrt{5x^2}$ and so on are radicals. The symbol $\sqrt{}$ is called a radical sign.

radicand. The quantity under a *radical* sign. For example, 7 in $\sqrt{7}$, and x^2y in $\sqrt{x^2y}$.

radius of a circle. A *line segment* with one endpoint the center of a *circle*. The other endpoint is on the circle.

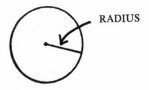

RADIUS

radius of a sphere. A *line segment* whose one endpoint is the center of the sphere and whose other endpoint is on the sphere.

RADII OF
A SPHERE

radix (ray'diks). Synonym for *base* (in a *notation system*). A base five system is called a system with a radix of five. Ten is the radix of our system of notation.

random sampling. Taking a *sample* from the population in which all members have the same chance of being included.

range. In *statistics,* the *absolute difference* between the greatest measure and the least measure in any set of *data.*

range of a relation or function. If a relation is a set of *ordered pairs*—(0, 1), (1, 2), (2, 3), (3,4)—the range of the relation is the set of second members of the number pairs. In this case the set {1, 2, 3, 4} is the range of this relation or function. See *domain.*

rate of interest. Usually expressed in percent form; for example, 6% per year. See *table of formulas p. 215*.

rate of speed. If a plane flies 1200 miles in 2 hours, the ratio of the number 1200 and 2 is usually called the rate and is expressed as 600 miles per hour.

ratio. The *quotient* of two numbers. It can be written $\frac{a}{b}$ or a:b where $b \neq 0$. See *fractions*.

Also an *ordered pair* of numbers. To compare two sets, we might try to match elements. We can say the ratio between the sets is 12 to 18, or 6 to 9, or 2 to 3. All name the same ratio.

RATIO 6 TO 9

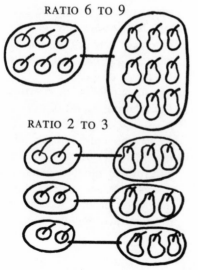

RATIO 2 TO 3

rational expression. An expression stated as the *quotient* of two *polynomial* expressions over the *integers*. It is understood that the denominator cannot be zero.

$$\frac{3x+1}{x}, \frac{3y}{18}, \frac{x \times 3x+1}{x+1}, x+1$$

are all rational expressions. See *rational number*.

rationalization. The *denominator* or *divisor* of a *rational expression*. The removal of the *radicals* in the denominator in an expression without changing the value. For example,

$$\frac{3}{\sqrt{5}} = \frac{3\sqrt{5}}{5}.$$

rational number. A number that can be expressed in the form of a *fraction* as $\frac{a}{b}$ where a and b are any *integers* and $b \neq 0$. Sometimes rational numbers are defined in terms of ordered pairs of integers: (a, b) where $b \neq 0$. Equality of rational numbers means (a, b) = (c, d) if and only if ad = bc. Addition of rational numbers means

(a, b) + (c, d) = (ad + bc, bd).

The rational number (a, 1) or $\frac{a}{1}$ is written a.

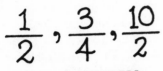

RATIONAL NUMBERS

rational number in arithmetic.
A *fractional number*.

ray. A *point* in a *line* divides the
line into 2 half-lines. A ray is
a half-line, together with the
point. The point is called the
endpoint of the ray. A ray is
shown as:

See *arrow*.

real numbers. The set of real
numbers consists of the set of
rational numbers and the set
of *irrational numbers*.

real plane. A *coordinate* system
on a plane in which an *ordered
pair* of *real numbers* can be
associated with every point on
the plane.

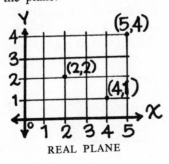

REAL PLANE

ream. A package of 500 sheets of
paper.

reasoning, mathematical. See *deductive reasoning; induction,
mathematical*.

reciprocal. See *multiplicative inverse*.

RECIPROCALS

rectangle. A *parallelogram* with
one angle a *right angle*. This
makes all the angles right
angles.

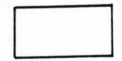

rectangular numbers. Numbers
that can be represented by dots
or other symbols in the shape
of a *rectangle*. The number 8
may be represented as

or

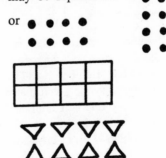

rectangular parallelepiped. A right *parallelepiped* with rectangular bases.

A RECTANGULAR
PARALLELEPIPED

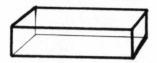

IS ALSO A RECTANGULAR
RIGHT PRISM

rectangular right prism. A right *prism* whose faces are rectangular regions.

reducing fractions to lowest terms. A phrase used to mean the removal of the *greatest common factor* of the *numerator* and *denominator* of a fraction. When the largest common factor of the numerator and denominator is 1, the fraction has been reduced to lowest terms, or simplest form.

 LOWEST
TERMS

redundant number. A number, the sum of whose factors (except the number itself), is greater than the given number. 18 is a redundant number because $1 + 2 + 3 + 6 + 9 = 21$, which is more than 18.

referent. The object or idea to which a name refers. In 37, "3" refers to or represents 3 groups of 10. The referent is the 3 groups of 10 things.

reflection. Mirroring an image or counterpart; one of the *invariant* properties of Euclidean *geometry*.

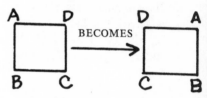

reflexive property of equality. For each number, a, a = a is a true statement.

reflex angle. Any angle whose measure is more than 180° and less than 360°.

REFLEX ANGLE

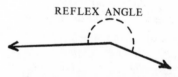

region of a plane. Part of a *plane*. The interior of a *simple closed curve* is a region. The picture shows a rectangular region bounded by a rectangle.

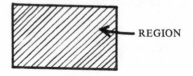

REGION

regrouping. Another name, in the elementary schools, for the *associative property for addition* and *for multiplication*.

$$3 + (4 + 6) = (3 + 4) + 6$$
$$3 \times (9 \times 4) = (3 \times 9) \times 4$$

regular polygon. A *polygon* in which all sides are the same length and all interior angles are the same measure.

REGULAR POLYGONS

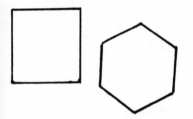

relation. A set of *ordered pairs*.

x	y	
1	2	(1,2)
2	4	(2,4)
3	6	(3,6)
4	8	(4,8)

relationship, one-to-one. See *correspondence*.

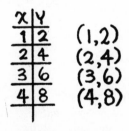

relative error. Ratio of the *greatest possible error* or *G.P.E.* to the total measure. If the relative error is given as a percent, then the relative error is called the percent of error.

$$\text{Relative error} = \frac{\text{G.P.E.}}{\text{measure}}$$

relatively prime whole numbers. Numbers whose only common factor is 1. For example, 5 and 9 are relatively prime numbers.

remainder. In $9 \div 2$, which means $9 = \square \times 2 + \triangle$, $\triangle$ is the remainder. $9 \div 2$ is $9 = 4 \times 2 + 1$, so 1 is the remainder. $\triangle = 1$.

11 ÷ 4 MEANS

$$11 = \square \times 4 + \triangle$$

PLACEHOLDER FOR FACTOR   PLACEHOLDER FOR REMAINDER

$$11 = \boxed{2} \times 4 + \triangle{3}$$

renaming numbers. A number has many names. $\frac{8}{10}$ may be renamed $\frac{4}{5}$. $5(2 + 3)$ may be renamed 25. 14 may be renamed $10 + 4$.

repeating decimal. A *decimal* in which one digit repeats itself endlessly or a group of digits repeat themselves endlessly:

.23333 . . .
.257257 . . .

Any repeating decimal can be expressed in the form $\frac{a}{b}$ when a and b are integers, and b $\neq$ 0. Therefore, a repeating decimal represents a rational number.

repetend. The name given to the *digit* or group of digits that repeat endlessly in the decimal form of a *rational number.* See *repeating decimal.*

replacement set. The *set* of numbers whose names are used as replacements for the *variable* in an *equation* or *inequality.*

result. The outcome of one or more *operations,* or the end in a proof.

resultant of two forces. One force which is equivalent to two forces. See *force, component of.*

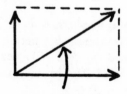

RESULTANT OF
TWO FORCES

revolution. Consider a *ray* with a fixed *endpoint.* If a ray moves about a fixed point in a *plane,* it will come back to its initial position. We say the ray has turned through one revolution.

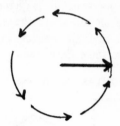

Rhind papyrus. A mathematical work of *Ahmes,* discovered in modern times by A. Henry Rhind. The main portion is now in the British Museum.

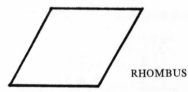

RHOMBUS

rhombus. A *parallelogram* with 2 adjacent sides equal in length. It can be shown that all four sides are the same length.

Riemann, Georg (ree′man), 1826–1866. A German mathematician and the founder of a *non-Euclidean geometry* which, like those of *Bolyai* and *Lobachevski,* was based on assuming a

GEORG
RIEMANN

postulate different from *Euclid's 5th or parallel postulate*. He replaced the parallel postulate of Euclid with the postulate: Through a given point outside a given line there are no parallels to the given line. That is, any pair of lines must meet.

Riemann was also one of the founders of *topology*.

right. Direction on the *number line* to describe *greater than*. A number associated with a point to the right of a second point is greater than the number associated with the second point. −6 is greater than −10.

right angle. An angle of 90°.

right triangle. A triangle, one of whose angles is a right angle.

ring. In geometry, the portion of a plane between 2 *concentric circles*. See *annulus*.

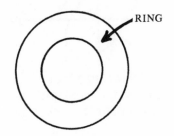

RING

rod. A unit of measure. 1 acre contains 160 square rods. See *table p. 217*.

rods. See *analogue computers, Montessori rods, Napier's bones, Stern rods*.

Roman numerals. The notation system used by the Romans. The first ten numerals are I II III IV V VI VII VIII IX X. Other symbols are: L(50), C(100), D(500) and M (1000).

root. A solution of an equation. 3 is a root of $2x = 6$ because $2 \times 3 = 6$. See *square root, cube root, quadratic formula*.

rotation. Turning around, as a wheel on its axis. One of the *invariant* properties.

ROTATION OF
COORDINATE AXES

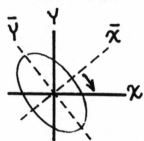

GEOMETRIC FIGURES ARE
ROTATED TO STUDY THEM
IN DIFFERENT POSITIONS

round angle. A rarely used term for an angle of 360°, sometimes called a perigon.

ROUND
ANGLE

rounded number. An approximate number. Usually a number expressed in some convenient unit so that its meaning in the situation can be more easily understood or used. 4,879,652 might be written as 5,000,000, rounded to the nearest million.

row. A line or arrangement running horizontally, as opposed to a *column* which is a vertical arrangement.

1 2 3 4 ROW
2
3
4

COLUMN

rule. Sometimes a rule in mathematics is a procedure, as a rule for the order of operations. Sometimes it is a definition, as the rule of signs in multiplying integers, Sometimes a rule is a formula. The rule for finding the perimeter of a square is $p = 4s$.

rule or ruler. A *straightedge* with graduations or a scale.

rule of signs. See *Descartes*.

Russell, Sir Bertrand, 1872–

An English mathematician and

SIR BERTRAND
RUSSELL

philosopher. Early in the 20th century he published many important mathematical works, among them "Principia Mathematica" with *A. N. Whitehead*.

S

S. Abbreviation for *surface*.

s. Abbreviation for side. s represents the length of a side. It is used in such *formulas* as p = 3s.

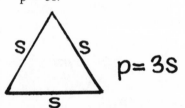

sample of a population. In *statistics*, a group of people selected at random from a population. Polls used in politics and TV program ratings use a sample group of people selected to represent a cross section of a larger population to which they belong.

sample point. One of the possible outcomes of an *event*, named by an *ordered pair* of numbers. See *sample space*.

sample space. In *statistics*, all the possible outcomes of an experiment. Each outcome is called a *sample point*.

Sand Reckoner, The. One of *Archimedes'* papers on arithmetic. In it he proves that no matter how large a number is—even a number representing all the grains of sand that would fill a sphere with its center at the earth's center, and its circumference touching the sun—it is possible to represent this number as a *finite* number.

satisfy. To fulfill conditions.

satisfy an equation. A number such as 5 satisfies the equation 2x + 3 = 13, because when x is replaced by 5, 2(5) + 3 = 13 is a true *statement*. A number satisfies an equation if a true statement is formed when the *variable* is replaced by the numeral for the number.

scalar. A number written in front of a *matrix* to show the operation of multiplication to be performed on every element in the matrix by that number.

$$2 \begin{pmatrix} 1 & 5 & 6 \\ 3 & 2 & 4 \end{pmatrix}$$

SCALAR

scale. A measuring device that is a set of units, usually equally spaced. Thermometers, rulers and balances for weighing are all scales. See also *scale drawing*.

scale drawing. One which is in direct *proportion* to the subject drawn. It may be smaller, as a map, equal in size, or larger than the original object, as a billboard.

scalene triangle (skay-leen′). A triangle with no two sides equal.

SCALENE TRIANGLE

scientific notation. A way of writing numbers by expressing a number as a product of two *factors*. One factor is an integral *power* of ten, and the other is a factor between 1 and 10. For example, 2,950,000 can be written 2.95×10^6.

score. The equivalent of 20. "Four score and seven years ago" is $4 \times 20 + 7 = 87$.

In testing, a score is the performance of an individual or a group, shown by a numeral, letter or other mark.

scruple. In *apothecaries' weight*, 20 grains. See *table p. 216*.

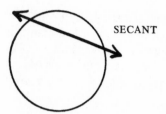

SECANT

secant of a circle. A line that intersects a circle at two points is called a secant.

second. A measure of time, $\frac{1}{60}$ of a minute. A measure of distance on the earth's surface, part of a *degree* of distance. See *table p. 218*.

An *ordinal number,* indicating a position in an *array*.

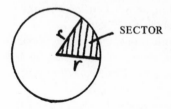

SECOND APPLE

section, golden. See *golden section*.

sector of a circle. Part of a circular *region* bounded by two *radii* and the *intercepted arc*.

SECTOR

segment. See *line segment.* Segment of a circle refers to the region bounded by an *arc* of the circle and its *chord.*

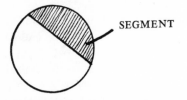

SEGMENT

selling price. The price of an item to the buyer, usually the *cost* of the item plus the *overhead,* plus the *profit* the merchant wishes to make.

semi. A prefix meaning *half.* A semicircle is one of the two half-arcs of a circle determined by the endpoints of a *diameter.*

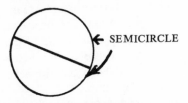

← SEMICIRCLE

sentence, mathematical. A sentence that uses numerals, symbols and sometimes words. It may be true or false. Two expressions with a symbol of numerical relationship between them. For example, the following are mathematical sentences:

$7 > 3$ (7 is greater than 3)
$4 + 2 = 6 + 0$
$7x + 3 = 17$
$x^2 + 3x + 2 = 0$
See *compound, conditional open sentence, connective.*

separation. The division of a *set* into two or more *subsets.*

$$\text{SET A} = \{1, 2, 3, 4, 5, 6\}$$
$$\text{SET B} = \{2, 4, 5, 6\}$$
$$\text{SET C} = \{1, 3\}$$

SUBSETS

septennial. Occurring every 7 years.

septillion. In the United States and France, 1 followed by 24 zeros. In England and Germany, 1 followed by 42 zeros.

sequence, number. A sequence is a set of numbers associated with the *counting numbers.* The numbers must be in a certain order. For example, 1, 3, 5, 7, 9 is a sequence of terms that can be associated with the positive integers 1, 2, 3, 4, and 5. There must be a rule for finding any term of the sequence. The sequence 1, 3, 5, 7, 9 progresses by 2. Its general term is $2n - 1$.

An *arithmetic progression* and

a *geometric progression* are both examples of number sequences.

A sequence is sometimes defined as a *function* whose *domain* is the *positive integers*.

series. The indicated sum of the terms of a *sequence*. For example, 1, 3, 5, 7 and 9 are terms of a sequence. $1 + 3 + 5 + 7 + 9$ is a series.

set. An *undefined term* in mathematics. The term set is useful in talking about collections or groups of objects. The objects may be things, numbers, ideas and so on. Each object in a set is called a *member* or *element* of the set. Sets are described

$$\{a, b, c, d\}$$

MEMBERS OF THE SET

by listing names of members, $\{1, 2, 3, 4, 5\}$. *Braces* are used to enclose the names of the members of a set. Sometimes a set is described by a *condition,* for example, the set of all *natural numbers* less than 6. It is only when we have made it clear which objects belong to the set and which do not, that we have a *well-defined set*.

set·builder notation. See *such that.*

set selector. Let the possible *replacements* for the *variable* x in the sentence $x + 2 = 5$ be the set $\{1, 2, 3, 4\}$.

If $x = 1$, $1 + 2 = 5$ (false).
If $x = 2$, $2 + 2 = 5$ (false).
If $x = 3$, $3 + 2 = 5$ (true).
If $x = 4$, $4 + 2 = 5$ (false).

Thus, the sentence $x + 2 = 5$ is called a set selector in that it sorts the set $\{1, 2, 3, 4\}$ into two sets, one set $\{1, 2, 4\}$ whose members make the sentence false, and the other set $\{3\}$ that makes the sentence true.

set theory. The branch of mathematics concerned with *sets,* the *operations* on sets and the *properties* concerning these operations on sets. Set theory has many applications in logic, chance and probability, geometry and the higher branches of mathematics.

sexagesimal system of numeration (sek'sa-jes'ih-mal). A numeration system using 60 as a base. See *Babylonian notation system.*

sextillion. In the United States and France, 1 followed by 21 zeros. In England and Germany, 1 followed by 36 zeros.

shadow reckoning. A method of

measuring heights by the sun's shadow used by the early Egyptians.

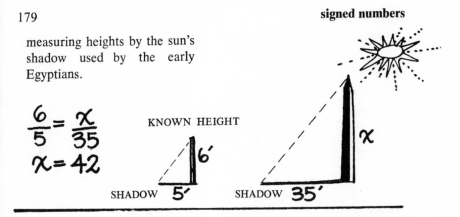

$$\frac{6}{5} = \frac{x}{35}$$

$$x = 42$$

KNOWN HEIGHT

6′

SHADOW 5′   SHADOW 35′

---

short ton. In *avoirdupois weight,* 2000 pounds, a ton.

sides of an angle. The two *rays* that comprise the angle are called sides.

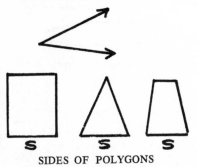

SIDES OF POLYGONS

sieve of Eratosthenes (e-ra-tos′ the-neez). A method worked out by *Eratosthenes* for finding all *prime numbers* less than a particular number. Write the numbers from 2 to the particular number. After 2, cross out every second number. The first

number left is a prime, 3, so cross out every third number. The next prime left is 5, so cross out every fifth number and continue.

2 3 4̸ 5 6̸ 7 8̸ 9̸
1̸0̸ 11 1̸2̸ 13 1̸4̸ 1̸5̸ 1̸6̸
17 1̸8̸ 19 2̸0̸ 2̸1̸ 2̸2̸
23 2̸4̸ 2̸5̸ 2̸6̸ 2̸7̸
2̸8̸ 29 3̸0̸

signed numbers. Also called *directed numbers.* A term commonly used to describe the set of the negative numbers (numbers less than zero), zero and the positive numbers (numbers greater than zero). A *number line* is usually used to picture the numbers.

significant digits. Those which are important in expressing the number of units used to find the measure of an object. The following *digits* are considered significant:

1. Each nonzero digit.

12

2. Each zero digit between nonzero digits.

102

3. Each zero digit which is not used only for the purpose of locating the decimal point.

102.0

similar figures. Two figures having the same shape, if not the same size.

SIMILAR FIGURES

similarity correspondence. The *correspondence* between *vertices* of two *polygons* in which the corresponding angles are *congruent* and the corresponding sides are proportional in measure.

simple closed curve. A closed curve which does not cross itself.

SIMPLE CLOSED CURVES

simple closed figure. See *closed plane figure*.

simple condition. A requirement expressed by an *open sentence*. In the *condition* x + 4 = 6, the replacement for x is 2. It answers the requirement because 2 + 4 = 6 is true.

simple event. A subject in an experiment of all possible happenings called an *event* space. When a penny is tossed it can land either head or tail up {H, T}. A simple event is {H} or {T}.

simple form of ratios. A *ratio* in which the two terms are *whole numbers* and the whole numbers have the number 1 as the *greatest common factor.*

$$3:7 \quad \frac{3}{7}$$

simple interest. See *interest.*

simple sentence. A mathematical statement with one thought. Some simple sentences are

$$4+3=7$$
$$4>3$$
$$4<5$$

simplify. To write a shorter form of a *numeral* or *algebraic expression.* For example, to simplify [2 (3 + 5) −7], do all the operations called for until the expression has reached its simplest form, 9. 5x is 2x + 3x in simpler form.

simultaneous equations. Two *linear equations* with *variables* whose *graphs* intersect at one point. They are said to have a

common *solution.* Some authors use "simultaneous equations" to mean a system of equations which may or may not have a common solution.

sine ratio of a right triangle. The *ratio* of the measure of the side opposite angle A to the measure of the *hypotenuse* is called the sine of the angle. The sine of ∠ A is usually abbreviated sin A.

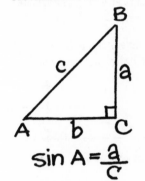

$$\sin A = \frac{a}{c}$$

skewed curve. A curve that lacks *symmetry* with respect to a vertical line. In statistics, a curve not perfectly *bell-shaped,* but

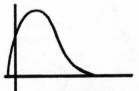

CURVE SKEWED
TO THE RIGHT

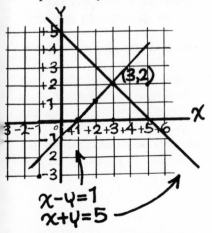

$$x-y=1$$
$$x+y=5$$

whose highest point is to the left of the *median* (negatively skewed) or to the right (positively skewed).

MEDIAN

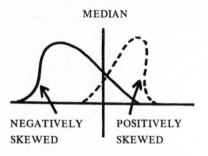

NEGATIVELY
SKEWED

POSITIVELY
SKEWED

skew lines. Two lines which do not lie in any one plane.

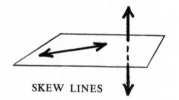

SKEW LINES

slant height of a right circular cone. The length of an element of a surface of the cone.

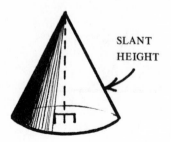

SLANT
HEIGHT

slide rule. An instrument for multiplying, dividing, extracting roots and obtaining powers of numbers mechanically through the use of sliding logarithmic scales.

slope. The rate at which a curve rises or falls per horizontal unit. The slope of a nonvertical line is expressed in terms of *coordinates* of any 2 points:

$$\text{slope} = \frac{(y_2 - y_1)}{(x_2 - x_1)}$$

small circle. See *circle, small; circle, great.*

smaller than. See *less than.*

solid figure. See *space figure.* A solid refers to a space figure.

SOME SOLID FIGURES ARE
CUBES, CONES AND SPHERES

solid geometry. See *space geometry.*

solidus (sol'ih-dus). The slash sometimes used instead of a bar when writing a fraction ¾.

solution. Any number from the *domain* (replacement set) of the *variable* which makes the *open sentence* a true statement. For example, from the set of numbers $\{1, 2, 3, 4, \ldots\}$ the number 4 is a solution of $3x + 2 = 14$ because $3 \times 4 + 2 = 14$.

solution set. The solution set or *truth set* of an *open sentence* is the set which contains all the solutions of the open sentence and no others.

solve. To find the *solution set* to a *mathematical sentence* involving *variables*.

soroban. A Japanese *abacus*.

space. The *set* of all *points*. A three-dimensional *region*.

space curve. A curve in space, such as a *helix*. The *intersection* of two surfaces.

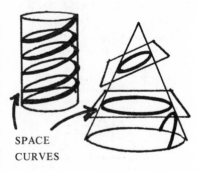

SPACE
CURVES

space figure. A set of points which may have one, two or three dimensions. *Cubes,*

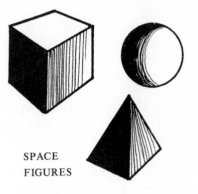

SPACE
FIGURES

spheres and *pyramids* are space figures. Sometimes they are called solids, solid geometrical figures or solid shapes.

space geometry. The study of three-dimensional space and *space figures*. Sometimes called solid geometry.

specific gravity. In a solid, the *ratio* of the weight per given *volume* to an equal volume of water.

$$\text{specific gravity} = \frac{\text{weight of given volume}}{\text{weight of same volume of water}}$$

speed. Distance traveled per unit of time. See *table of formulas p. 215.*

speed of light. Light travels at approximately 186,000 miles per second. The symbol for the speed of light is c.

speed of sound. In dry air at 32°F. or 0°C. (the point at which water freezes), sound travels at approximately 760 miles per hour.

sphere. A *set* of *points* in *space* such that every point is equidistant from a point called the *center.* See *table of formulas p. 214.*

spiral. A coil shape on a *plane* surface.

square. A *rectangle* having two adjacent sides of equal length. It can be shown that all four sides are the same length.

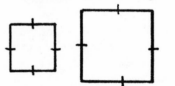

square numbers. Numbers which can be represented by dots in the form of a square.

square of a number. A number raised to the second *power.* $5^2 = 25$. A number multiplied by itself: $5 \times 5 = 25$.

square root of a number. A number that, when raised to the second *power,* produces the given number. For example, a square root of 9 is 3 because $3^2 = 9$. The symbol for square root is $\sqrt{\ }$. See *principal*

square root, table of square roots p. 221.

squaring the circle. See *circle, squaring the.*

stadium paradox of Zeno. One of his four *paradoxes,* in which he stated that a given interval of time or space can be equal to twice that same amount of time or space.

IF 3 ROWS OF PEOPLE ARE SITTING LIKE THIS:

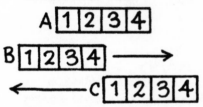

AND AT THE SAME INSTANT THE PEOPLE IN ROW B MOVE TO THE RIGHT, WHILE THOSE IN ROW C MOVE TO THE LEFT, UNTIL THEY ARE SEATED LIKE THIS:

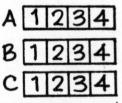

B HAS PASSED ALL 4 OF C, BUT ONLY 2 OF A.
THUS A GIVEN INTERVAL OF TIME OR SPACE IS EQUAL TO ITS DOUBLE.

standard. A basis for comparison.

standard description of a solution set. A *solution set* whose *elements* are not tabulated or listed. The solution set of the *condition* x > ⅔ can only be described as {x|x > ⅔}: read, "The set of all x's *such that* each x is greater than ⅔."

standard deviation. See *deviation, standard*.

standard form. A form generally accepted as a way of writing an *algebraic expression* so that the *exponents* of one of the *variables* are in descending order:

$$ax^4 + bx^3 + cx^2 + ax + e$$

standard form of a quadratic equation. A *quadratic equation* in which the term containing the *second power* is written first. $8x^2 + \frac{2}{3}x + 6 = 0$. The general form $ax^2 + bx + c = 0$ where a, b, c are *real numbers* and $a \neq 0$.

standard name of a numeral. In the base ten system, for example, 347 is in standard form. It means $300 + 40 + 7$. See *expanded notation*.

standard number of a set. The *cardinal number* of *elements* in a *set*.

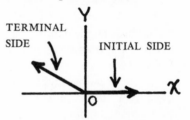

$$SET\ A = \{a, b, c, d\}$$

STANDARD ↑
NUMBER **4**

standard position of an angle. In trigonometry an angle is said to be in standard position if the *vertex* is the point of the origin of the x-and y-*axes* and the initial side of the angle is on the positive x-axis.

TERMINAL SIDE

INITIAL SIDE

standard units of measure. Units of measure that are accepted by agreement. They are uniform and unvarying. See *tables pp. 216–220*.

statement. A *mathematical sentence* that is either true or false, but not both.

statistics, descriptive. The branch of mathematics that collects information known as *data* and tabulates and analyzes it. See *bell-shaped curve*.

statute mile (also called land mile). A land measure, 5280 feet in length. In many parts of the world a *kilometer* is used as the standard measure of land distance. See *table p. 249.*

Stern blocks. A set of colored blocks named for educator Catherine Stern. They are graduated in size, each ¾″ larger than the previous one, and similar to the blocks developed by Countess *Montessori.*

Stevinus, Simon (steh-vee′nus), 1584–1620. A Dutch mathematician known for his work in applied mathematics, particularly the triangle of *forces.* He used the idea of *exponents* to show the *power* to which a quantity is to be raised. His were among the first books devoted to the theory of *decimals.* His symbolism was quite awkward compared with today's. For example, 6.879 would be written: 6⓪8①7②9③.

stone. In English measure, the equivalent of 14 pounds.

straight angle. An angle of 180°.

STRAIGHT ANGLE

straightedge. An instrument used for making straight lines in geometric drawings. Unlike a *ruler* it has no measuring scale.

straight line. See *line.*

structure of a system. There are different mathematical systems. Each has its own structure. A number system has a *set* of *elements* (numbers); it may have two operations ($+$ and $\times$), and certain properties of the operations, such as the *commutative property.*

suan pan (swan pan). A Chinese *abacus.*

subscript. A numeral, letter or word written to the right and just below another numeral. It may be used to indicate the *base* of the *notation system* of the numeral. The numeral 432_{FIVE} indicates the name of the number in *base five.*

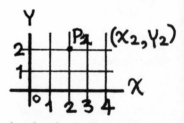

A subscript is also used to distinguish *points* and *coordinates,* and to distinguish terms, such as a_1, a_2, a_3 and so on.

subset. If every *element* of *set* A is also a member of set B, then set A is a subset of set B. We say that set A is included in set B. For example, if set A consists of the letters a, b, c, and set B consists of the letters a, b, c and d, then set A is a subset of set B. See *proper subset*.

SUBSET

substitution in algebra. The usual reference is to the *replacement* of a *variable* by a numeral.

substitution in codes. See *codes*.

subtend in geometry. To be opposite to, as a chord subtends the arc it cuts on a circle.

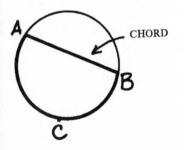

SUBTENDED ARC, $\overset{\frown}{ACB}$

subtraction. Subtraction is the *inverse* of *addition*. For example, $7 - 4$ is a number, n, so that $n + 4 = 7$. Since $3 + 4 = 7$; $7 - 4 = 3$.

$$\square + 3 = 7$$
$$\boxed{4} + 3 = 7$$
$$7 - 3 = 4$$

In general, if a and b are two whole numbers and a is greater than or equal to b, $a - b$ is a number, c, such that $c + b = a$. $a - b = c$ means $c + b = a$. See *subtrahend, minuend, operation*.

subtrahend. The number or *term* to be subtracted.

$$7 - 3 \nwarrow \text{ SUBTRAHEND}$$

succession. *Numerals, terms* or *operations* which follow each other in a definite order.

successor. Any *term* that immediately follows any other term in a *sequence*. In 1, 2, 3, 4, 5, . . . the successor of 1 is 2, the successor of 2 is 3 and so on.

such that. Usually referred to in *set-builder notation*. The symbol for "such that" is |. $\{x \mid x + 5 = 7\}$ is read: The set of all x's such that $x + 5 = 7$. The symbol $\{ | \}$ is called a set builder.

sum. In addition, the result of adding 2 or more numbers or *addends*.

sum property of "less than." For all real numbers a, b, c, if $a < b$ then $a + c < b + c$. Often called *addition property of inequalities*.

sunya. The Hindu word for zero. Arabian mathematicians translated it as "sifr," meaning empty, which became "cipher." Later it became the Latin word "zephirum," which eventually became zero.

supplementary angles. Two angles whose sum is 180°. Each is the supplement of the other.

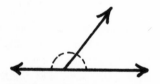

SUPPLEMENTARY ANGLES

surd. Sometimes used for an *irrational number*. $\sqrt{7}, \sqrt[3]{12}, \sqrt{1/2}$ are examples of surds. The *radicands* are *rational*.

surface. A surface consists of *sets* of *points*. Usually, surface is *undefined* in geometry. There

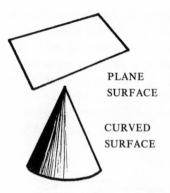

PLANE SURFACE

CURVED SURFACE

are plane surfaces such that a straight line joining any two of its points lies completely in the plane. There are curved surfaces of which no part is a plane. A surface may consist of plane and curved surfaces.

syllogism (sil'loh-jiz'm). In logic, an argument, usually with 3 parts:

1. A major premise or general statement.

2. A minor premise or specific statement.

3. A conclusion based on the above two.

For example:

1. All persons living in New York City live in New York State (major premise).

2. Henry lives in New York City (minor premise).

3. Henry lives in New York State (conclusion).

Sylvester, James, 1814–1897. An English mathematician and professor. Although his best known contributions are in higher algebra, he wrote valuable papers on the theory of numbers and prime numbers. While at Johns Hopkins, where he was the first professor of mathematics, he founded the "American Journal of Mathematics" in 1878.

symbol. A letter, numeral or mark which represents a number, operation or relation. See *table of symbols pp. 210–212.*

SYMBOLS

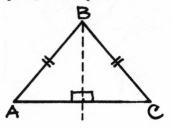

symmetric. A relationship with the property that if a is related to b, then b is related in the same manner to a. If a = b then b = a.

symmetry in geometry. The *correspondence* of parts of a figure on opposite sides of a point, line or plane. The *isosceles triangle* is symmetric with respect to the line through vertex B, perpendicular to the base AC.

synthesis. The combination of elements into a whole. *Analysis* and synthesis are two methods used in mathematical thinking.

T

T. T-score in statistics is a standardized score. The *mean* is 50 and the *standard deviation* is 10.

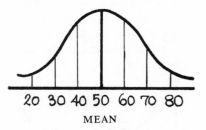

MEAN

t. Abbreviation for *temperature, ton, time.*

When used in a *formula* such as d = rt, t is a *variable* which stands for a numeral.

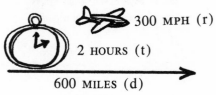

300 MPH (r)

2 HOURS (t)

600 MILES (d)

table 190

table. An arrangement of numerals, letters or signs, usually in *rows* and *columns,* to show facts or relationships between them in a compact form. For example, the cost of 1 to 5 gallons of gasoline at 28 cents a gallon may be shown in a table.

NUMBER OF GALLONS	1	2	3	4
COST	.28	.56	.84	1.12

tangent of an acute angle. In a right triangle, the *ratio* of the measure of the side opposite an acute angle to the measure of the side *adjacent* to the same acute angle.

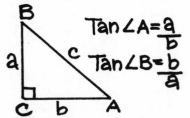

$$\text{Tan} \angle A = \frac{a}{b}$$
$$\text{Tan} \angle B = \frac{b}{a}$$

tangent to a circle. A *line* in the *plane* of a *circle* that intersects the circle in only one *point.*

tangram. A puzzle made by Chinese mathematicians about 4000 years ago that showed how shapes are related. It was basically a square made of 7 pieces. Hundreds of pictures can be made with these 7 pieces.

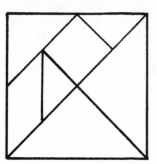

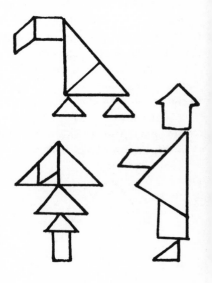

target set. In *statistics,* the set of numbers, people, etc. about which information is desired.

Tartaglia, Niccolo (tar-tal'ya), 1499–1557. An Italian mathematician whose solution for *cubic equations* is often credited unjustly to *Cardano.* His work on arithmetic and numbers gives an excellent account of methods in use at that time and is one of our chief sources of information. He also described the business customs of the day, and a number of mathematical puzzles for amusement, some of which go back to Hindu and Arabic mathematicians. Many of his puzzles were included in later books.

temperature. The amount of heat in a body or in the air, as measured by a thermometer. The two standard units are the *Fahrenheit* scale and the *centigrade* or *Celsius* scale.

ten. A number. The Latin word for ten is "decem." See *decimal system, base ten.*

terminal point. To describe a movement from point A to point B, we may use a *directed line segment* or *vector.* Point A is called the initial point and point B the terminal point of the line segment.

terminal side of an angle. See *standard position of an angle.*

terminating. Coming to an end. See *decimal, terminating.*

term of an expression. A numerical expression is a numeral, or numerals joined with symbols of operation:

$$7, \frac{(8+2)}{3}, 6 \times 7.$$

Algebraic expressions include numerical expressions and expressions formed with variables: $x, 3y, n^2, \frac{x+7}{9}$.

Each part of an expression written as a sum is called a term. In $(x-y) + \frac{(x-y^2)}{x}$ -7, the terms are $x-y$, $\frac{(x-y^2)}{x}$ and -7. In the *polynomial* $3n^2 + 6n - 9$, the terms are $3n^2$, $6n$ and -9.

terms of a fraction. The *numerator* and *denominator* of a fraction.

TERMS

terms of a proportion. Any one of the *means* or *extremes*. ³⁄₄ = ⁶⁄₈. The terms are 3, 4, 6 and 8. See *proportion*.

EXTREMES

MEANS

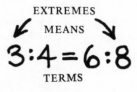

3:4 = 6:8

TERMS

terms of a sequence. The *members* of the *range* of a *sequence*.

1, 3, 5, 7, 9

TERMS

ternary (tur'neh-ree). Having to do with 3; having three *variables*. The ternary system of notation is *base* three.

tetrahedron (tet-ra-heed'ron). A *polyhedron* of 4 faces. A *regular* tetrahedron is a pyramid whose base and faces are *congruent equilateral* triangles.

TETRAHEDRON

Thales (thay'lees), 640–546 B.C. The founder of the first Greek school of mathematics and philosophy. He was the teacher of *Pythagoras,* and probably the first person to insist on *proof* in geometry. He is the first man known to have shown that the base angles of an *isosceles* triangle are *congruent* and vertical angles are congruent.

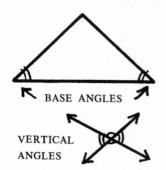

BASE ANGLES

VERTICAL ANGLES

theorem. A *proposition* to be proved. Theorems proved true are used in proofs to prove other theorems true or false.

thermometer. An instrument used to measure *temperature*.

times. A word commonly used to indicate multiplication. 3×4 is read three 4's or three times four. It also means $4 + 4 + 4$. The symbols for times are $\times$ and $\cdot$. With *variables*, no multiplication sign is needed, as in 3x, abc and $14x^2$. Parentheses can also indicate multiplication, $x(a + b)$.

tolerance. The allowable error in a given measurement. If a part has a given measure of 5.125″, the error allowable when making the part may be .005″ more than or less than the actual measure of 5.125″. The standard way of writing the tolerance allowed is 5.125 "±.005," which means that any measure between 5.120″ and 5.130″ would be acceptable.

ton. A measure of weight equal to 2000 lbs., sometimes called a short ton. A *long ton* is 2240 lbs. A register ton is a unit of ship capacity, not weight. It is 100 cubic feet.

A cargo ton is a unit of volume used for freight. It is 40 cubic feet. A kip is a half ton or 1000 lbs.

topology. Scientifically called *analysis situs;* popularly called rubber-sheet geometry. One of the most recent branches of mathematics, it deals with place and position, and not quantity or measure. It concerns those properties of figures, like insides, outsides and direction, which do not change no matter how the figures are bent, stretched or distorted. In topology, these two figures

are the same in the sense that they each have 1 inside and 1 outside:

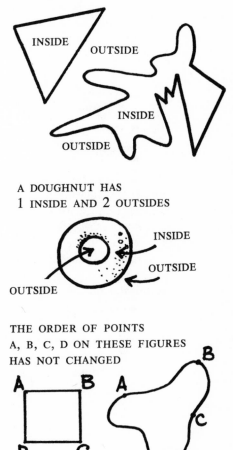

A DOUGHNUT HAS
1 INSIDE AND 2 OUTSIDES

THE ORDER OF POINTS
A, B, C, D ON THESE FIGURES
HAS NOT CHANGED

See *Klein bottle, Möbius strip, Brouwer's problem, torus, Euler, Riemann.*

torus

torus (toh′rus). A doughnut-shaped 3-dimensional figure used in *topology*. Ordinarily we think of the hole as inside the doughnut, but in topology the hole is considered to be outside.

trajectory. The curve or path of a projectile, such as a bullet, as it goes through the air; also, the *curve* or *surface* which cuts all the curves or surfaces of a given *plane* or *space* at a constant angle.

transcendental number. An *irrational number,* but not an *algebraic* one. Examples of transcendental numbers are π (3.1415926 . . .) and e, the symbol for the base of natural *logarithms* (2.7182818 . . .). *Cantor* proved that transcendental numbers cannot be counted.

transform. To change the form of an *expression.* The word can also be used to refer to the expression or term which has been changed. For example,

when ½ is changed to 50%, 50% can be called the transform.

transforming formulas. Solving *literal equations* for any *variable.* For example, in the formula for finding the area of a triangle, A = ½ab where A is the area, a is the measure of

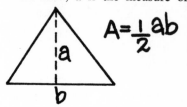

the altitude of the triangle, b is the measure of the base of the triangle. If a is to be found, the tranformation of

$$A = \frac{1}{2}ab \text{ becomes } a = \frac{A}{(\frac{1}{2}b)}.$$

transitive property of congruence. In geometric figures:

If △ ABC ≅ △ DEF and
△ DEF ≅ △ GHJ, then
△ ABC ≅ △ GHJ.

This is true of any geometric figures.

transitive property of equality.

If a = b and
b = c then
a = c.

See *equality*.

translation. An exact duplication of a geometric figure. One of the *invariant* properties of *Euclidean geometry.*

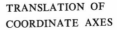

TRANSLATION OF ABCD

TRANSLATION OF
COORDINATE AXES

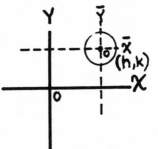

transposition in codes. One of the principal ways of making a code by changing the position of the letters.

transversal. A straight *line* intersecting two or more lines at 1 point on each line.
Line AB is the transversal.

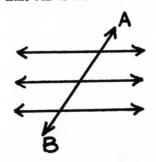

trapezium (tra-pee′zee-um). A *quadrilateral,* no two of whose sides are *parallel.*

TRAPEZIUM

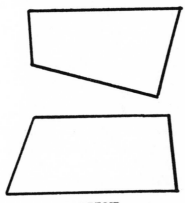

TRAPEZOID

trapezoid. A *quadrilateral* with two, and only two, opposite sides *parallel.*

trapezoidal prism. A right *prism* whose bases are trapezoids.

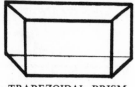

TRAPEZOIDAL PRISM

triangle. The *union* of *line segments* AB, BC and AC. A *closed plane figure* with three sides. Triangles are classified by the relationship of the sides (see *equilateral, isosceles, scalene*) or by the measure of the angles (see *acute, obtuse, right angles*). See also *table of formulas p. 213.*

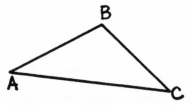

triangular numbers. Numbers that can be represented by dots in the form of a triangle. The first three triangular numbers are 3, 6, 10.

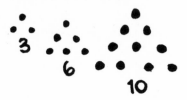

triangular pyramid. A pyramid that has a triangle as its base.

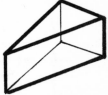

TRIANGULAR PYRAMID

triangular right prism. A right *prism* whose bases are triangles.

TRIANGULAR RIGHT PRISM

trichotomy property of real numbers (try-kot'oh-mee). States that for any two *real numbers*, a and b, only one of the following is true:

1. $a = b$
2. $a < b$
3. $a > b$

trigonometry. The branch of mathematics that deals with the sides and angles of triangles and their measurements and relations. It also includes the study of trigonometric functions and their properties.

trihedral angle. A *polyhedral an-*

TRIHEDRAL
ANGLE

gle with three faces.

trillion. A hundred billion, represented by 1 followed by 12 zeros in the United States and France, and 1 followed by 18 zeros in England and Germany.

trinomial. A *polynomial* of three terms. For example,
$$x^2 - 3x + 7.$$

trisection of the angle. Division of an angle into 3 equal parts. One of 3 classic problems of ancient Greek mathematics which cannot be solved using *Euclidean tools.* Attempting to find a solution, the Greeks discovered new mathematical concepts. See *cube problem; circle, squaring the.*

trivial. Of little importance. For any *natural number,* the trivial *divisors* are 1 and the number itself. The trivial divisors of 12 are 1 and 12.

Troy system of weights. A system for measuring precious metals. See *table p. 216.*

true length. The actual length of an object. Because all measurement is approximate, there is always a difference between the true length and the *measured length.*

truth element. In a mathematical sentence containing a *variable,* one of the *elements* of the *replacement set* that makes the sentence true; the solution or one of the solutions.

In
$$x + 2 = 5,$$
$$3 + 2 = 5 \text{ is true;}$$
so 3 is a truth element for the variable x.

truth set. A *set* whose *elements* are the solutions for a mathematical *sentence;* often called *solution set.* See *set selector.*

truth value. In *logic* each given statement has a truth value. The truth value may be true or false. The truth value of $3 + 4 = 8$ is false. The truth value of "The surface of the earth is curved" is true.

twelve-base for numeration. See *duodecimal system.*

twice. Two times, or double, as twice the quantity.

twin primes. Two *prime numbers* with a difference of 2. 3 and 5, 11 and 13, 17 and 19 are examples of twin primes.

two, system of numeration. See *binary system.*

0,1

A BINARY SYSTEM OF
NUMERATION HAS TWO SYMBOLS

U

U. The *universal set* is often denoted by U.

Uccello, Paolo (oo-chel′loh), 1397–1475. An Italian artist who first used perspective. He was the first to make drawings on a *plane* surface, like paper or canvas, which gave the impression of having depth, or a third *dimension*.

undefined terms. We define a new *term* by means of simpler terms, and these are defined by still simpler terms. We finally reach terms that cannot be defined in a simpler way. Our definitions rest upon these undefined terms. Some undefined terms in geometry are *point* and *line*.

unequal. Not equal. The symbol is ≠. In $4 + 6 \neq 11$, we have the statement that 4 plus 6 not equal to 11. In set A ≠ set B, we mean the sets do not have exactly the same elements. See *inequality, equivalent*.

unit. "One" is a unit. The unit *column* in our *Hindu-Arabic notation system* refers to the first column to the left of the decimal point. In 729, the unit *digit* is 9.

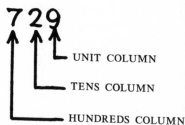

union. The joining or combining of two or more things.

The union of two *sets* A and B is the set of elements which belongs to A, to B, or to both A and B. For example, if set A = {1, 2, 3, 4} and set B = {3, 4, 5, 6}, then the union of the two sets is the set {1, 2, 3, 4, 5, 6}. The union of set A and set B is usually written A ∪ B (read: A union B or A cup B). The union can be used to define the sum of two numbers. Let

K = {a, b, c} and

L = {d, e, f, g}, then

{a, b, c} ∪ {d, e, f, g} =
{a, b, c, d, e, f, g}

The number associated with set K is 3, with set L is 4, and with K ∪ L is 7. The sum of two numbers which are associated with two *disjoint sets* is the number associated with their union. See *addition, cup, join.*

unique. One and only one. The sum of two numbers is unique.

5+4=9

There is one and only one sum of two numbers. If a number is said to *correspond* to a unique point on a line, it means that the number corresponds to one and only one point.

unique factorization property. Every *positive integer* can be expressed as the product of *prime factors* in one and only one way, regardless of the order of the factors.

3 × 2 × 2 = 12
2 × 3 × 2 = 12
2 × 2 × 3 = 12

uniqueness. If an operation is performed on any two elements of a set and the result is one and only one element, the operation has the property of uniqueness. For example, the sum of 7 + 8 is the *unique* number 15. There is one and only one number that is the sum of any two *real numbers.* The operations of addition and multiplication have this *property* in the set of real numbers.

unit angle. An angle of some measure that by common agreement will be the standard unit of angular measurement by which to measure all other angles.

unite. To join or combine so as to form a whole.

unit fraction. A fraction whose *numerator* is one and whose *denominator* is an *integer.* For example, $\frac{1}{2}$, $\frac{1}{5}$.

unit of measurement. A standard used, such as a pound, an inch, a gram etc. Sometimes the word "unit" is used with a numeral, as

6 units of work,

3 units of length.

units, fundamental. The units of length, mass and time that form the basis for a system of measurement. For example:

the *centimeter,* the *gram* and the *second* are the fundamental units of the *cgs* or *metric system.*

unity element. Another name for the *identity element.*

universal set. The *set* from which all the *subsets* are selected in a discussion. For example, the *whole numbers* from 1 to 100 may be the universal set of our discussion. We may then discuss even numbers less than 100 and odd numbers less than 100, or some other subset. The universal set is often designated set *U.*

universe. The *set* of all *replacements* for a *variable* in a mathematical *condition.* See *universal set.*

unknown or unknown quantity. A symbol or a *placeholder* in a mathematical sentence. The unknown holds a place for the name of any element in the *replacement set.* The unknown is more commonly called a *variable.* In $5x + 3 = 13$, x is the unknown, or variable.

UNKNOWNS

$$\square, \triangle, x, y$$

unlike fractions. Fractions with different *denominators:* $\frac{2}{3}$, $\frac{2}{5}$.

V

V. The Roman numeral for five. Abbreviation for *volume.*

v. A *variable* used in *formulas* involving *velocity, volt.*

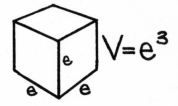

valid. Reasonable for a set of *assumptions.*

value. The value of a variable is any number in the *domain* of the variable. It is also the number named by an *expression* formed from numerals and signs of operations. The value of the expression $3(5 + 2)$ is 21.

21 is the standard name for $3(5 + 2)$. If an expression includes a *variable,* the value is the number named by the expression when the variable is replaced by a numeral. The value of $3x^2 + 7x$, when x is 2, is 26. See *place value, absolute value.*

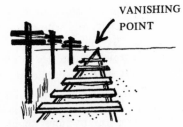

VANISHING POINT

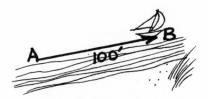

vanishing point. In a perspective drawing, the place where parallel lines seem to come together.

variable. A letter or other *placeholder* in a mathematical expression. It may represent any *element* in a given *set* of elements. The set of elements is called the *domain* of the variable. Sometimes a variable is called an unknown. In $x^2 + 3x + 2 = 0$, x is the variable.

variable sentence (often called an *open sentence*). A mathematical sentence that contains at least one *variable*. It cannot be judged true or false until its variable is replaced by a numeral. $x + 5 = 7$ is a variable sentence. If x is replaced by 2, it is a true sentence. 2 is called a solution of $x + 5 = 7$.

variance. In *statistics*, the number which shows the amount of spread in a set of *scores*.

variation. See *direct variation, inverse variation*.

vector. In the drawing, there has been a movement, or displacement, from point A to point B. The displacement can be described as:
1. A *magnitude* of 100'.
2. A direction, parallel to the shore. To show the displacement geometrically, we use the *directed line segment* AB or vector AB. Point A is called the *initial point* and point B the *terminal point*. If from point B the boat moves to C, it seems logical that the vectors $\overrightarrow{AB}$ followed by $\overrightarrow{BC}$ are the same as a move directly from A to C. This is an example of "addition" of vectors. We say $\overrightarrow{AB} + \overrightarrow{BC} = \overrightarrow{AC}$. $\overrightarrow{AC}$ is called the vector resultant and can replace $\overrightarrow{AB}$ and $\overrightarrow{BC}$ as

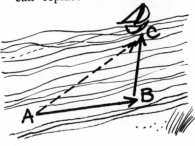

forces. So from a geometric representation, an algebra of vectors develops.

When the algebraic properties of vectors are abstracted from the geometry in which they originate, we enter vector space. See *force, components of.*

vector quantity. A quantity that has both *magnitude* and direction. See *vector.*

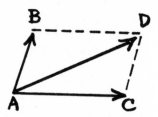

PARALLELOGRAM OF VECTORS

vectors, parallelogram of. If two vectors $\overrightarrow{AB}$ and $\overrightarrow{AC}$ are represented as two sides of a *parallelogram,* the other two sides can be drawn. The diagonal of the parallelogram is the vector *resultant* $\overrightarrow{AD}$. See *vector, force.*

velocity. The unit of distance traveled, in a specified direction, per unit of time. See *table of formulas p. 215.*

Venn, John, 1834–1923. An English mathematician who worked in statistics, probability and logic, and whose name is given to Venn diagrams.

Venn diagrams. Diagrams to picture *sets* and the relationships between sets. The sets are represented by circles and their interiors, or by any shapes.

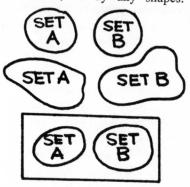

Sometimes the shapes are placed within a rectangle.

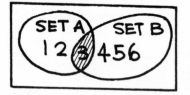

If set A = {1, 2, 3} and set B = {3, 4, 5, 6} the diagram shows that their *intersection* is 3. Other relationships can easily be shown by Venn diagrams. See *subset, union, complementary set.*

VERTEX

vertex of an angle. The point of intersection of the two *rays* that form the angle.

vertex of a polygon. The point of intersection of any two adjacent sides of the polygon.

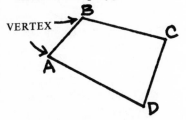

VERTEX

vertical. A vertical line is perpendicular to a horizontal line in the same plane.

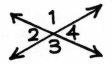

VERTICAL LINE

HORIZONTAL LINE

vertical angles. Angles formed by two intersecting lines. Angles 1, 3 and 2, 4 are vertical angles.

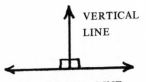

vertical form. An arrangement to facilitate computations. The vertical form of $80 + 6 + 23$ is

80
6
23

vertices (ver'tih-sees). In *topology*, the points where the lines in a *network* cross. A, B, C, D E are vertices. See *vertex of a polygon.*

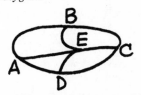

Vieta, François (vyay'ta'), 1540–1603. A wealthy French lawyer and official whose hobby was mathematics. His many contributions included the use of letters as symbols for known and unknown quantities in algebra. He was the first to show that the value of π could be found from a formula instead of a complicated geometric figure. He wrote on equations and infinite converging series, and did research in analysis and trigonometry. The Spanish accused him of sorcery because during a war between

France and Spain he deciphered the Spanish code which contained hundreds of symbols.

vinculum (vihn'ku-lum). A bar written over two or more quantities to show *grouping.* $\overline{8+4}$ ÷ 3 means that the addition of 8 and 4 should be performed first. See *brackets, braces, parentheses.*

volt. A practical standard unit for measuring electrical force. 1 volt is needed to drive 1 *ampere* through 1 *ohm.*

volume. The number of *cubic* units in a solid. The volume of this rectangular solid is 24 cubic units.

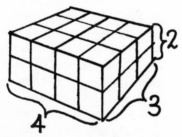

In sound, the loudness measured in *decibels.* See *table of formulas pp. 212–214.*

von Neumann, John, 1903–1957. One of the outstanding mathematicians of this century. Born in Hungary, he came to the United States in 1930 to teach mathematical physics at Prince-

JOHN
VON NEUMANN

ton University. At 28 he wrote a book on the quantum theory, which was one step in developing atomic energy. He built one of the first electronic *computers,* designed many nuclear devices and contributed much to *game theory.*

W

w. The abbreviation for *watt, width, weight.*

It is used as a *variable* in such *formulas* as A = lw.

$$A = lw$$

Wallis, John, 1616–1703. English mathematician, physician, clergyman and philosopher.

His publications on *conic sections* clarified the work of *Descartes*. He introduced the first systematic use of formulas in his writing on algebra. His most important work was the "Arithmetic of Infinities," in which he extended the methods of Descartes and *Cavalieri*.

JOHN
WALLIS

watt. A standard unit for measuring electrical power, equal to 1 *joule* per second.

week. A period of time; seven days. A work week is the number of working days in a week.

Weierstrass, Karl (vie'er-straws), 1815–1897. One of the greatest German mathematicians of the nineteenth century, a teacher of *Kowalewski* and *Cantor*. He worked in mathematical *analysis,* in the theory of *functions* and on ideas that had troubled mathematicians since ancient times: *infinity* and *irrational numbers.* His work eventually influenced the production of atomic energy and our present ideas of *infinite series.*

weight. The pull of gravity on a body. For common measures of weight, see *tables pp. 216–220.*

well-defined set. A *set* described so that it is clear whether any *element* is or is not a member of the given set. "The set of all funny books," and "the set of all pretty girls" are not well defined because there can be differences of opinion about what or who should be included. "The set of all books on this table," and "the set of all girls over 6 feet tall in this school" are well defined.

ALFRED
NORTH
WHITEHEAD

Whitehead, Alfred North, 1861–1947. English philosopher and mathematician who taught at the universities of London and

Harvard. He used mathematical analysis in philosophy and in 1910 wrote his major work, "Principia Mathematica," with *Bertrand Russell.* In it, the very structure of mathematics was probed. It is considered one of the greatest contributions to logic since *Aristotle.*

whole numbers. The set of numbers {0, 1, 2, 3, 4 . . .} *Natural numbers,* or *counting numbers,* are usually considered not to include zero.

width. Measure from side to side.

Wiener, Norbert (ween'er), 1894–1964. An American scientist who coined the term *cybernetics.* He believed that many thought processes in the human brain could be determined mathematically and adapted for machines, thus becoming the founder of a new branch of science.

X

X. The Roman numeral for ten.

x. A symbol. A *variable,* or *unknown* quantity.

$$2x = 10$$

x-axis. To locate any *point* in a *plane* by means of a pair of numbers, we select two intersecting lines in the plane as *axes.* The horizontal axis is called the x-axis. See *abscissa.*

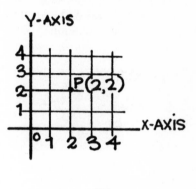

Y

y. A symbol. A *variable,* or *unknown* quantity.

$$x^2 + y^2 = 16$$

y-axis. On a *coordinate plane,* the vertical *axis.* See *x-axis, coordinates.*

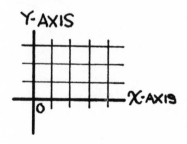

yard. A unit of *linear measurement* equal to 36 inches. See *table pp. 216–217.*

year. The period of time it takes the earth to make one complete orbit of the sun, approximately 365 days, 5 hours, 48+ minutes. The extra hours, minutes and seconds are lumped into an extra day every four years, which we call a "leap year."

Z

z. A symbol. A *variable*, or *unknown* quantity.

zenith. The point of the celestial sphere directly above the observer.

ZENITH

Zeno, 495–435 B.C. A Greek mathematician and philosopher best known for his *paradoxes,* all of which deal with the idea of *infinity* of time and motion. It took mathematicians over 2000 years to solve them. Of the eight paradoxes he originated, four are known: The dichotomy, *Achilles and the tortoise, the arrow in motion* and the *Stadium.*

zero. The number associated with the *empty set.* It is denoted by 0.

zero in division. Suppose a is a number, not zero. There are three possibilities.

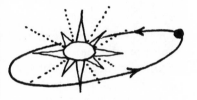

$$1.\frac{0}{a} \quad 2.\frac{a}{0} \quad 3.\frac{0}{0}$$

1. $\frac{0}{a} = c$ means $a \times c = 0$. Since $a \neq 0$, then $c = 0$. Therefore, $\frac{0}{a} = 0$.

2. $\frac{a}{0} = c$ means $a = 0 \times c$. But $0 \times c = 0$ for all numbers, and cannot equal a, which is not zero. Therefore $\frac{a}{0}$ is meaningless.

3. $\frac{0}{0} = n$ means $0 = 0 \times n$.

But this is true for any number n. For this reason we say $\frac{0}{0}$ is indeterminate. Division by zero cannot be done. See *zero property of addition, zero in multiplication, additive identity*.

zero in multiplication. The product of zero and any number is zero. For all numbers, a, $a \times 0 = 0 \times a = 0$. For example, $125 \times 0 = 0 \times 125 = 0$.

-3 -2 -1 0 +1 +2 +3

zero point. That point on a *number line associated* with zero. It separates the points associated with the *positive numbers* on the right and the *negative numbers* on the left.

zero power. The value of any *real number* except zero raised to the zero *power* is always 1. Any number with an *exponent* of zero is 1. $3^0 = 1$; $127.50^0 = 1$; $\left(\frac{15}{27}\right)^0 = 1$.
For any real number a, $a^0 = 1$, where $a \neq 0$.

zero property of addition. There exists a *unique* number, zero, such that for any number a, $a + 0 = 0 + a = a$. For example, $6 + 0 = 0 + 6 = 6$. Zero is called the *additive identity* in addition.

zone. In geometry, the part of the surface of a *sphere* bounded by the two intersections of *parallel planes* with the sphere.

ZONE

TABLE OF SOME COMMONLY USED MATHEMATICAL SYMBOLS

$+$	plus; add; positive
$-$	minus; subtract; negative
$\pm$	plus or minus
$\times$	times; multiply; cross
$\cdot$	times; multiply
$\div$	divide
$\overline{)}$	divide
$-, /$	divided by (as $\frac{a}{b}$)
$o, *$	undefined operation
$\sqrt{}$	square root
$\sqrt[3]{}$	cube root
$\sqrt[n]{}$	nth root
$\ldots$	between two numerals or letters, omission; at the end of a series or sequence, and so on

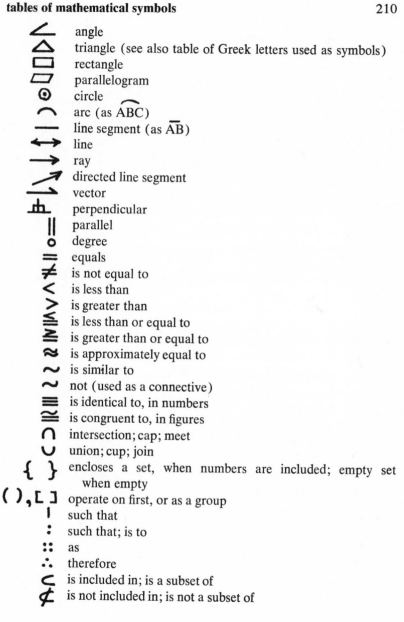

∠	angle
△	triangle (see also table of Greek letters used as symbols)
▭	rectangle
▱	parallelogram
⊙	circle
⌒	arc (as $\overset{\frown}{ABC}$)
──	line segment (as $\overline{AB}$)
↔	line
→	ray
➚	directed line segment
→	vector
⊥	perpendicular
‖	parallel
°	degree
=	equals
≠	is not equal to
<	is less than
>	is greater than
≤	is less than or equal to
≧	is greater than or equal to
≈	is approximately equal to
∼	is similar to
∼	not (used as a connective)
≡	is identical to, in numbers
≅	is congruent to, in figures
∩	intersection; cap; meet
∪	union; cup; join
{ }	encloses a set, when numbers are included; empty set when empty
( ),[ ]	operate on first, or as a group
|	such that
:	such that; is to
::	as
∴	therefore
⊆	is included in; is a subset of
⊄	is not included in; is not a subset of

$|n|$ absolute value of n
$[$ $)$ half-closed interval
$($ $]$ half-open interval
%   percent
!   factorial
$'$ foot; minute
$''$ inch; second
∞ infinity
O   open point
●   closed point

LETTERS USED AS SYMBOLS FOR SETS AND SUBSETS

C   the set of counting numbers
D   the set of real numbers
I   the set of integers
I_n the set of negative integers
I_p the set of positive integers
N   the set of natural numbers
R   the set of rational numbers
$\bar{R}$ the set of irrational numbers
R_a the set of rational numbers of arithmetic

GREEK LETTERS COMMONLY USED AS SYMBOLS

α (alpha) to denote first in a series
β (beta) to denote second in a series
γ (gamma) to denote interior angle
Δ (delta) with a variable to denote a small increase in the value of the variable
$\in$ (epsilon) stands for "is a member of"
$\notin$ (epsilon) stands for "is not a member of"
Θ (theta) stands for "any angle"
π (pi) equals 3.1416 ...
Σ (sigma) stands for "summation"
σ (sigma) stands for "the sum of the divisors"
ϕ (phi) stands for "empty set"
ρ (rho) stands for "first element in ordered pair of polar coordinates"

TABLE OF SOME COMMONLY USED FORMULAS

Symbols used in formulas unless otherwise indicated.

A	area
a	altitude, apothem
B	area of a base
b_1, b_2	measure of bases
c	circumference
d	diameter
e	measure of an edge
h	height
l	length
n	number of sides
p	perimeter
r	measure of a radius
S	surface area
s	measure of a side
V	volume
w	width
π	pi

FORMULAS FOR PLANE FIGURES

CIRCLE
circumference: $c = 2\pi r; c = \pi d$
area: $A = \pi r^2; A = \left(\dfrac{d}{2}\right)^2$

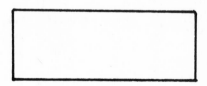

ELLIPSE
area: $A = \frac{1}{2}$ length of major axis $\times$ $\frac{1}{2}$ length of minor axis) $\times \pi$

PARALLELOGRAM
area: $A = ab$

RECTANGLE
perimeter: $p = 2(l + w)$
area: $A = lw$

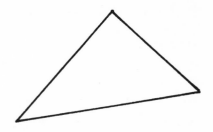

REGULAR POLYGON
perimeter: $p = ns$
area: $A = \frac{1}{2}\ ans$; $A = \frac{1}{2}\ ap$

SQUARE
perimeter: $p = 4s$
area: $A = lw$; $A = s^2$

TRAPEZOID
area: $A = \frac{1}{2}(b_1 + b_2)$

TRIANGLE
area: $A = \frac{1}{2}ab$
perimeter: Where a, b and c are the measure of the sides: $p = a + b + c$

EQUILATERAL TRIANGLE
perimeter: $p = 3s$

PYTHAGOREAN PROPERTY
Where c = hypotenuse and a and b = the measure of the sides opposite the acute angles of a right triangle: $c^2 = a^2 + b^2$

FORMULAS FOR SPACE FIGURES

RIGHT CIRCULAR CONE
Where r = the measure of a radius of the base:
volume: $V = \frac{1}{3}\ Bh$; $V = \frac{1}{3}\ \pi r^2 h$

CUBE
surface: $S = 6e^2$
volume: $V = e^3$

RIGHT CIRCULAR CYLINDER
Where r = the measure of a radius of a base:
surface: $S = 2\pi r(r + h)$
volume: $V = \pi r^2 h$

RECTANGULAR RIGHT PRISM

surface: $S = 2(lw + hw + lh)$
volume: $V = lwh$

RIGHT PRISM

volume: $V = Bh$
Where a = the measure of an apothem of a base: $V = \frac{1}{2} aph$

TRIANGULAR RIGHT PRISM

Where a = the measure of an altitude of a triangle that determines the base, b = measure of the base of the triangle:
surface: $S = ab + hp$
volume: $V = \frac{1}{2} abh$

REGULAR PYRAMID

Where a = the measure of an apothem of the base and p = the perimeter of the base:
volume: $V = \frac{1}{3} Bh; V = \frac{1}{6} aph$

SQUARE REGULAR PYRAMID

volume: $V = \frac{1}{3} (e^2h)$

TRIANGULAR PYRAMID

Where a = the measure of an altitude of the triangle that determines the base, and b = the measure of the base:
volume: $V = \frac{1}{6} abh$

SPHERE

surface: $S = 4\pi r^2$
volume: $V = \frac{4}{3}\pi r^3$

FORMULAS FOR COMPUTATIONS

AMOUNT
Where a = total amount, p = principal and i = interest: $a = p + i$

AVERAGE
Where a = average, t = total and n = number of items: $a = \dfrac{t}{n}$

COST
Where c = total cost, n = number of items and p = price of each item: $c = np$.
For finding the price of a single item when the total cost is known:

$$p = \frac{c}{n}$$

DISTANCE
Where d = distance, r = rate and t = time: $d = rt$
For falling objects: $d = 16t^2$

INTEREST
Where i = interest, p = principal, r = rate and t = time: $i = prt$

PERCENTAGE
Where p = percentage, b = base and r = rate: $p = br$

SELLING PRICE
Where s = selling price, c = cost, o = overhead and p = profit:
$s = c + o + p$

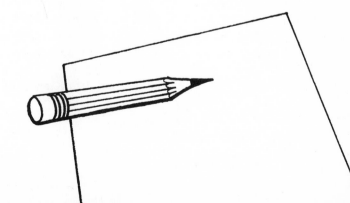

TABLES OF WEIGHTS AND MEASURES

AVOIRDUPOIS WEIGHT

$27\frac{11}{32}$ grains (gr.)	1 dram (dr.)
16 drams	1 ounce (oz.), $437\frac{1}{2}$ grains
16 ounces	1 pound (lb.), 256 drams, 7,000 grains
100 pounds	1 hundredweight (cwt.), 1,600 ounces
112 pounds	1 long hundredweight (1.cwt.)
20 hundredweight	1 ton (t.), 2,000 pounds
20 long hundredweight	1 long ton (t.), 2,240 pounds

TROY WEIGHT

24 grains (gr.)	1 pennyweight (dwt.)
20 pennyweights	1 ounce (oz. t.) 480 grains
12 ounces	1 pound (lb. t.), 240 penny-weights, 5,760 grains

APOTHECARIES' WEIGHT

20 grains (gr.)	1 scruple (s. ap. or ℈)
3 scruples	1 dram (dr. ap. or ʒ), 60 grains
8 drams	1 ounce (oz. ap. or ℨ), 24 scruples, 480 grains
12 ounces	1 pound (lb. ap. or ℔), 96 drams, 288 scruples, 5,760 grains)

LINEAR MEASURE

12 inches (in.)	1 foot (ft.)
3 feet	1 yard (yd.), 36 inches
$5\frac{1}{2}$ yards	1 rod (rd.), $16\frac{1}{2}$ feet
40 rods	1 furlong (fur.), 220 yards, 660 feet
8 furlongs	1 statute mile (mi.), 1,760 yards, 5,280 feet
3 miles	1 league (l.), 5,280 yards

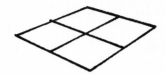

SQUARE MEASURE

144 square inches (sq. in.) ...	1 square foot (sq. ft.)
9 square feet	1 square yard (sq. yd.), 1,296 square inches
30¼ square yards	1 square rod (sq. rd.), 272¼ square feet
160 square rods	1 acre (A.), 4,840 square yards
640 acres	1 square mile (sq. mi.), 3,097,600 square yards
36 square miles	1 township

CUBIC MEASURE

1,728 cubic inches (cu. in.) ..	1 cubic foot (cu. ft.)
27 cubic feet	1 cubic yard (cu. yd.)
144 cubic inches	1 board foot
128 cubic feet	1 cord

CHAIN MEASURE

Gunter's, or Surveyor's, Chain

7.92 inches (in.)	1 link (li.)
100 links	1 chain (ch.)
80 chains	1 mile (mi.)

Engineer's Chain

12 inches	1 link
100 links	1 chain
52.8 chains	1 mile

SURVEYOR'S AREA MEASURE

625 square links (sq. li.)	1 square rod or square pole (sq. p.)
16 square rods	1 square chain (sq. ch.), surveyor's
10 square chains	1 acre (A.)
640 acres	1 square mile (sq. mi.)
36 square miles	1 township

LIQUID MEASURE

4 gills (gi.)	1 pint (pt.)
2 pints	1 quart (qt.), 8 gills
4 quarts	1 gallon (gal.), 8 pints, 32 gills
31½ gallons	1 barrel (bbl.), 126 quarts
2 barrels	1 hogshead (hhd.), 63 gallons, 252 quarts

APOTHECARIES' FLUID MEASURE

60 minims (min. or ℳ)	1 fluid dram (fl. dr. or f℥)
8 fluid drams	1 fluid ounce (fl. oz. or f℥), 480 minims
16 fluid ounces	1 pint (o.), 128 fluid drams, 7,680 minims
8 pints	1 gallon (C.), 128 fluid ounces, 1,024 fluid drams

DRY MEASURE

2 pints (pt.)	1 quart (qt.)
8 quarts	1 peck (pk.), 16 pints
4 pecks	1 bushel (bu.), 32 quarts, 64 pints
105 quarts	1 barrel (bbl.), dry measure, 7,056 cubic inches

ANGULAR AND CIRCULAR MEASURE

60 seconds (″)	1 minute (′)
60 minutes	1 degree (°)
90 degrees	1 quadrant (quad.)
180 degrees	1 straight angle
4 quadrants	1 circle

NAUTICAL MEASURE

6 feet	1 fathom (fath.)
100 fathoms	1 cable's length (ordinary)
120 fathoms	1 cable's length (U.S. Navy)
10 cable lengths	1 nautical mile
1 nautical mile	1.1515 statute miles
60 nautical miles	1 degree (deg. or °)

THE METRIC SYSTEM

LINEAR MEASURE

10 millimeters	1 centimeter
10 centimeters	1 decimeter
10 decimeters	1 meter
10 meters	1 decameter
10 decameters	1 hectometer
10 hectometers	1 kilometer

SQUARE MEASURE

100 sq. millimeters	1 sq. centimeter
100 sq. centimeters	1 sq. decimeter
100 sq. decimeters	1 sq. meter
100 sq. meters	1 sq. decameter
100 sq. decameters	1 sq. hectometer
100 sq. hectometers	1 sq. kilometer

CUBIC MEASURE

1000 cu. millimeters	1 cu. centimeter
1000 cu. centimeters	1 cu. decimeter
1000 cu. decimeters	1 cu. meter

LIQUID MEASURE

10 milliliters	1 centiliter
10 centiliters	1 deciliter
10 deciliters	1 liter
10 liters	1 decaliter
10 decaliters	1 hectoliter
10 hectoliters	1 kiloliter

WEIGHTS

10 milligrams	1 centigram
10 centigrams	1 decigram
10 decigrams	1 gram
10 grams	1 decagram
10 decagrams	1 hectogram
10 hectograms	1 kilogram
100 kilograms	1 quintal
10 quintals	1 ton

CONVERSION TABLE—METRIC INTO ENGLISH SYSTEM

centimeter .... 0.3937 inch
meter .... 39.37 inches (exactly)
square centimeters .... .1549997 square inch
square meter .... 1.195985 square yards
hectare .... 2.47104 acres
cubic meter .... 1.3079428 cubic yards
liter .... .264178 gallons
liter .... 1.05671 liquid quarts
liter .... .908102 dry quart
hectoliter .... 2.83782 bushels
gram .... 15.432356 grains
kilogram .... 2.204622341 pounds, avoirdupois
inch .... 2.540005 centimeters
yard .... .9144018 meter
square inch .... 6.451626 square centimeters
square yard .... .8361307 square meter
acre .... .404687 hectare
cubic yard .... .7645594 cubic meter
gallon .... 3.785332 liters
liquid quart .... .946333 liter
dry quart .... 1.101198 liters
bushel .... 35.23833 liters
grain .... .064798918 gram
pound, avoirdupois .... .45359237 kilogram

Table of Square Roots

N	$\sqrt{N}$	N	$\sqrt{N}$	N	$\sqrt{N}$	N	$\sqrt{N}$	N	$\sqrt{N}$	N	$\sqrt{N}$
1	1.000	51	7.141	101	10.050	151	12.288	201	14.177	251	15.843
2	1.414	52	7.211	102	10.100	152	12.329	202	14.213	252	15.875
3	1.732	53	7.280	103	10.149	153	12.369	203	14.248	253	15.906
4	2.000	54	7.348	104	10.198	154	12.410	204	14.283	254	15.937
5	2.236	55	7.416	105	10.247	155	12.450	205	14.318	255	15.969
6	2.449	56	7.483	106	10.296	156	12.490	206	14.353	256	16.000
7	2.646	57	7.550	107	10.344	157	12.530	207	14.388	257	16.031
8	2.828	58	7.616	108	10.392	158	12.570	208	14.422	258	16.062
9	3.000	59	7.681	109	10.440	159	12.610	209	14.457	259	16.093
10	3.162	60	7.746	110	10.488	160	12.649	210	14.491	260	16.124
11	3.317	61	7.810	111	10.536	161	12.689	211	14.526	261	16.155
12	3.464	62	7.874	112	10.583	162	12.728	212	14.560	262	16.186
13	3.606	63	7.937	113	10.630	163	12.767	213	14.595	263	16.217
14	3.742	64	8.000	114	10.677	164	12.806	214	14.629	264	16.248
15	3.873	65	8.062	115	10.724	165	12.845	215	14.663	265	16.279
16	4.000	66	8.124	116	10.770	166	12.884	216	14.697	266	16.310
17	4.123	67	8.185	117	10.817	167	12.923	217	14.731	267	16.340
18	4.243	68	8.246	118	10.863	168	12.962	218	14.765	268	16.371
19	4.359	69	8.307	119	10.909	169	13.000	219	14.799	269	16.401
20	4.472	70	8.367	120	10.955	170	13.038	220	14.832	270	16.432
21	4.583	71	8.426	121	11.000	171	13.077	221	14.866	271	16.462
22	4.690	72	8.485	122	11.045	172	13.115	222	14.900	272	16.492
23	4.796	73	8.544	123	11.091	173	13.153	223	14.933	273	16.523
24	4.899	74	8.602	124	11.136	174	13.191	224	14.967	274	16.553
25	5.000	75	8.660	125	11.180	175	13.229	225	15.000	275	16.583
26	5.099	76	8.718	126	11.225	176	13.267	226	15.033	276	16.613
27	5.196	77	8.775	127	11.269	177	13.304	227	15.067	277	16.643
28	5.292	78	8.832	128	11.314	178	13.342	228	15.100	278	16.673
29	5.385	79	8.888	129	11.358	179	13.379	229	15.133	279	16.703
30	5.477	80	8.944	130	11.402	180	13.416	230	15.166	280	16.733
31	5.568	81	9.000	131	11.446	181	13.454	231	15.199	281	16.763
32	5.657	82	9.055	132	11.489	182	13.491	232	15.232	282	16.793
33	5.745	83	9.110	133	11.533	183	13.528	233	15.264	283	16.823
34	5.831	84	9.165	134	11.576	184	13.565	234	15.297	284	16.852
35	5.916	85	9.220	135	11.619	185	13.602	235	15.330	285	16.882
36	6.000	86	9.274	136	11.662	186	13.638	236	15.362	286	16.912
37	6.083	87	9.327	137	11.705	187	13.675	237	15.395	287	16.941
38	6.164	88	9.381	138	11.747	188	13.711	238	15.427	288	16.971
39	6.245	89	9.434	139	11.790	189	13.748	239	15.460	289	17.000
40	6.325	90	9.487	140	11.832	190	13.784	240	15.492	290	17.029
41	6.403	91	9.539	141	11.874	191	13.820	241	15.524	291	17.059
42	6.481	92	9.592	142	11.916	192	13.856	242	15.556	292	17.088
43	6.557	93	9.644	143	11.958	193	13.892	243	15.588	293	17.117
44	6.633	94	9.695	144	12.000	194	13.928	244	15.620	294	17.146
45	6.708	95	9.741	145	12.042	195	13.964	245	15.652	295	17.176
46	6.782	96	9.798	146	12.083	196	14.000	246	15.684	296	17.205
47	6.856	97	9.849	147	12.124	197	14.036	247	15.716	297	17.234
48	6.928	98	9.899	148	12.166	198	14.071	248	15.748	298	17.263
49	7.000	99	9.950	149	12.207	199	14.107	249	15.780	299	17.292
50	7.071	100	10.000	150	12.247	200	14.142	250	15.811	300	17.321

log π = .4971   log 4 π = 1.0992   log ⅓ π = .6221

N	0	1	2	3	4	5	6	7	8	9
10	0000	0043	0086	0128	0170	0212	0253	0294	0334	0374
11	0414	0453	0492	0531	0569	0607	0645	0682	0719	0755
12	0792	0828	0864	0899	0934	0969	1004	1038	1072	1106
13	1139	1173	1206	1239	1271	1303	1335	1367	1399	1430
14	1461	1492	1523	1553	1584	1614	1644	1673	1703	1732
15	1761	1790	1818	1847	1875	1903	1931	1959	1987	2014
16	2041	2068	2095	2122	2148	2175	2201	2227	2253	2279
17	2304	2330	2355	2380	2405	2430	2455	2480	2504	2529
18	2553	2577	2601	2625	2648	2672	2695	2718	2742	2765
19	2788	2810	2833	2856	2878	2900	2923	2945	2967	2989
20	3010	3032	3054	3075	3096	3118	3139	3160	3181	3201
21	3222	3243	3263	3284	3304	3324	3345	3365	3385	3404
22	3424	3444	3464	3483	3502	3522	3541	3560	3579	3598
23	3617	3636	3655	3674	3692	3711	3729	3747	3766	3784
24	3802	3820	3838	3856	3874	3892	3909	3927	3945	3962
25	3979	3997	4014	4031	4048	4065	4082	4099	4116	4133
26	4150	4166	4183	4200	4216	4232	4249	4265	4281	4298
27	4314	4330	4346	4362	4378	4393	4409	4425	4440	4456
28	4472	4487	4502	4518	4533	4548	4564	4579	4594	4609
29	4624	4639	4654	4669	4683	4698	4713	4728	4742	4757
30	4771	4786	4800	4814	4829	4843	4857	4871	4886	4900
31	4914	4928	4942	4955	4969	4983	4997	5011	5024	5038
32	5051	5065	5079	5092	5105	5119	5132	5145	5159	5172
33	5185	5198	5211	5224	5237	5250	5263	5276	5289	5302
34	5315	5328	5340	5353	5366	5378	5391	5403	5416	5428
35	5441	5453	5465	5478	5490	5502	5514	5527	5539	5551
36	5563	5575	5587	5599	5611	5623	5635	5647	5658	5670
37	5682	5694	5705	5717	5729	5740	5752	5763	5775	5786
38	5798	5809	5821	5832	5843	5855	5866	5877	5888	5899
39	5911	5922	5933	5944	5955	5966	5977	5988	5999	6010
40	6021	6031	6042	6053	6064	6075	6085	6096	6107	6117
41	6128	6138	6149	6160	6170	6180	6191	6201	6212	6222
42	6232	6243	6253	6263	6274	6284	6294	6304	6314	6325
43	6335	6345	6355	6365	6375	6385	6395	6405	6415	6425
44	6435	6444	6454	6464	6474	6484	6493	6503	6513	6522
45	6532	6542	6551	6561	6571	6580	6590	6599	6609	6618
46	6628	6637	6646	6656	6665	6675	6684	6693	6702	6712
47	6721	6730	6739	6749	6758	6767	6776	6785	6794	6803
48	6812	6821	6830	6839	6848	6857	6866	6875	6884	6893
49	6902	6911	6920	6928	6937	6946	6955	6964	6972	6981
50	6990	6998	7007	7016	7024	7033	7042	7050	7059	7067
51	7076	7084	7093	7101	7110	7118	7126	7135	7143	7152
52	7160	7168	7177	7185	7193	7202	7210	7218	7226	7235
53	7243	7251	7259	7267	7275	7284	7292	7300	7308	7316
54	7324	7332	7340	7348	7356	7364	7372	7380	7388	7396
N	0	1	2	3	4	5	6	7	8	9

$\log \pi = .4971$ $\log 4\,\pi = 1.0992$ $\log \frac{1}{3}\,\pi = .6221$

N	0	1	2	3	4	5	6	7	8	9
55	7404	7412	7419	7427	7435	7443	7451	7459	7466	7474
56	7482	7490	7497	7505	7513	7520	7528	7536	7543	7551
57	7559	7566	7574	7582	7589	7597	7604	7612	7619	7627
58	7634	7642	7649	7657	7664	7672	7679	7686	7694	7701
59	7709	7716	7723	7731	7738	7745	7752	7760	7767	7774
60	7782	7789	7796	7803	7810	7818	7825	7832	7839	7846
61	7853	7860	7868	7875	7882	7889	7896	7903	7910	7917
62	7924	7931	7938	7945	7952	7959	7966	7973	7980	7987
63	7993	8000	8007	8014	8021	8028	8035	8041	8048	8055
64	8062	8069	8075	8082	8089	8096	8102	8109	8116	8122
65	8129	8136	8142	8149	8156	8162	8169	8176	8182	8189
66	8195	8202	8209	8215	8222	8228	8235	8241	8248	8254
67	8261	8267	8274	8280	8287	8293	8299	8306	8312	8319
68	8325	8331	8338	8344	8351	8357	8363	8370	8376	8382
69	8388	8395	8401	8407	8414	8420	8426	8432	8439	8445
70	8451	8457	8463	8470	8476	8482	8488	8494	8500	8506
71	8513	8519	8525	8531	8537	8543	8549	8555	8561	8567
72	8573	8579	8585	8591	8597	8603	8609	8615	8621	8627
73	8633	8639	8645	8651	8657	8663	8669	8675	8681	8686
74	8692	8698	8704	8710	8716	8722	8727	8733	8739	8745
75	8751	8756	8762	8768	8774	8779	8785	8791	8797	8802
76	8808	8814	8820	8825	8831	8837	8842	8848	8854	8859
77	8865	8871	8876	8882	8887	8893	8899	8904	8910	8915
78	8921	8927	8932	8938	8943	8949	8954	8960	8965	8971
79	8976	8982	8987	8993	8998	9004	9009	9015	9020	9025
80	9031	9036	9042	9047	9053	9058	9063	9069	9074	9079
81	9085	9090	9096	9101	9106	9112	9117	9122	9128	9133
82	9138	9143	9149	9154	9159	9165	9170	9175	9180	9186
83	9191	9196	9201	9206	9212	9217	9222	9227	9232	9238
84	9243	9248	9253	9258	9263	9269	9274	9279	9284	9289
85	9294	9299	9304	9309	9315	9320	9325	9330	9335	9340
86	9345	9350	9355	9360	9365	9370	9375	9380	9385	9390
87	9395	9400	9405	9410	9415	9420	9425	9430	9435	9440
88	9445	9450	9455	9460	9465	9469	9474	9479	9484	9489
89	9494	9499	9504	9509	9513	9518	9523	9528	9533	9538
90	9542	9547	9552	9557	9562	9566	9571	9576	9581	9586
91	9590	9595	9600	9605	9609	9614	9619	9624	9628	9633
92	9638	9643	9647	9652	9657	9661	9666	9671	9675	9680
93	9685	9689	9694	9699	9703	9708	9713	9717	9722	9727
94	9731	9736	9741	9745	9750	9754	9759	9763	9768	9773
95	9777	9782	9786	9791	9795	9800	9805	9809	9814	9818
96	9823	9827	9832	9836	9841	9845	9850	9854	9859	9863
97	9868	9872	9877	9881	9886	9890	9894	9899	9903	9908
98	9912	9917	9921	9926	9930	9934	9939	9943	9948	9952
99	9956	9961	9965	9969	9974	9978	9938	9987	9991	9996
N	0	1	2	3	4	5	6	7	8	9

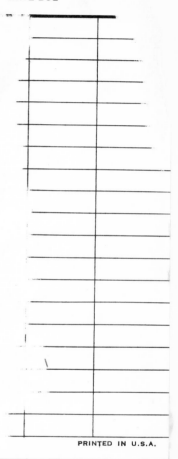

DATE DUE

PRINTED IN U.S.A.